Humanism and the Art of Medicine

A NEW CENTURY OF HEALTH

Soka Gakkai Malaysia

First Edition, 1999
Reprinted 2000, 2004, 2005, 2006, 2007

Humanism and the Art of Medicine
A New Centurty of Health

by Daisaku Ikeda

Published by Soka Gakkai Malaysia (SGM)
Wisma Kebudayaan SGM
243, Jalan Bukit Bintang, 55100 Kuala Lumpur, Malaysia
Tel: 603-2141 2003

Translation: The SGI Newsletter

Art Design: Chew Meng Tatt

Printed in Malaysia by Gainwell Enterprise

Contents

A Healthy Life is a Creative Life

Participants in this discussion on
' Humanism and the Art of Medicine:
A New Century of Health'
are SGI President Ikeda, Soka Gakkai
Doctors' Division Leaders Dr Shuhei Morita
and Dr Hiroyuki Toyofuku

SGI President Ikeda (right) together with Soka Gakkai Doctors' Division Leaders Dr Shuhei Morita (centre) and Dr Hiroyuki Toyofuku (left) at their discussion session.

PRESIDENT IKEDA: There is a great interest in the subject of health, isn't there?

MORITA: Yes. These days, I am constantly astonished at how well-informed everyone is about the latest medical research. When people come to see me seeking medical advice, they often ask questions, such as "How effective is interferon against Hepatitis C?" or, "Is it true that brain tumours can now be 'operated on' with a so-called 'gamma knife[1]', obviating the need for conventional surgery?" They certainly keep us doctors on our toes!

TOYOFUKU: There is a deluge of information about health available now on television, in the newspapers, and in magazines. So much, in fact, that it is perhaps difficult to judge what information is really pertinent. Some of the 'data' are actually produced by people who are trying to exploit the new 'health boom' for their own profit, and there are also many unscientific ideas floating around out there.

MORITA: We can also see that not only people who are ill, but those who are quite healthy as well, are very interested in so-called health foods, and in new diets.

---

1. *Gamma* knife: A newly developed technology in which brain tumours can be destroyed by bombardment with Cobolt 60 gamma rays without surgery.

PRESIDENT IKEDA: Health is a universal desire of human beings. No matter how wealthy or powerful one is, health, after all, is the most precious thing. There was once a man who had worked his way up from a penniless youth to one of the wealthiest people in the world. He fell ill and confessed that he would give all his riches to be young and healthy once more. He did not mind being poor again, as long as he had the health and the strength to work. I think we can all appreciate that.

Buddhism recognises illness as one of the most basic sufferings that human beings experience — as we can see from its inclusion in the four sufferings of birth, old age, sickness and death. In seeking to free people from this suffering, both Buddhism and medicine share a common goal.

What is the secret to living fully and vigorously day after day? Let us consider this question from the perspectives of Buddhism and medical science. I hope we can keep the discussion from becoming too technical, ensuring a simple and clear dialogue that all can readily understand.

MORITA: I will certainly try, but keeping things simple is really the hardest thing to do!

TOYOFUKU: On the other hand, worrying about it is not good for our health, either!

Fifteen Thousand Diseases

PRESIDENT IKEDA: Let us just be natural. Allow me to begin by posing a few basic questions on behalf of our readers. First, how many diseases are there?

TOYOFUKU: We have named about fifteen thousand diseases.

PRESIDENT IKEDA: My! That's a lot.

MORITA: Well, each disease can have several different names, depending on where it occurs in the body, its cause, its process of development and its symptoms.

TOYOFUKU: For example, there are more than two-hundred-and-fifty kinds of tuberculosis alone, including tuberculosis of the lungs, tuberculosis of the lymph nodes, spinal caries (a degenerative disease of the spinal cord) and tuberculosis meningitis (which affects the membrane covering the brain).

PRESIDENT IKEDA: Is stiffness of the shoulders a disease?

TOYOFUKU: No, things like stiff shoulders or stomach pains are what we call symptoms. Many different diseases can cause these symptoms.

PRESIDENT IKEDA: What kind of diseases will probably increase in the future?

MORITA: We are now seeing an increase in diseases caused by environmental pollution, in AIDS and new types of viruses, such as Ebola. There is also a danger of contracting diseases through contaminated pharmaceutical products or as a result of drug-related side-effects.

TOYOFUKU: Mental and psychological disorders are also on the rise. Gastric ulcers, asthma and temporary baldness (alopecia areata) are frequently caused by mental or emotional stress, for example. And, there is a strong relationship between one's mental state and the three major adult diseases, cancer, heart disease and stroke.

PRESIDENT IKEDA: The link between the mind and disease, the mind and health, are a point where Buddhism and medicine converge. The Buddhist scriptures also present many ways of categorising illness. In the Gosho, Nichiren Daishonin writes of four hundred and four maladies of the body and eighty-four thousand kinds of illnesses of the mind, the latter of which arise from the three poisons of greed, anger and stupidity (*WND*, pg 1111)[2]. He also says, "Illnesses of the mind vary greatly in severity." (Ibid)

Buddhism is not simply a kind of spiritualism or an abstract theory. Buddhists throughout the ages have focused squarely on the reality of physical and mental illnesses, and sought to relieve the suffering of illness from the dual perspective of Buddhism and medicine. Still, it is only natural that Buddhism concerns itself primarily with the role of the mind. And as stress-related illnesses increase in the future, the relationship between the mind and health in general will be spotlighted all the more.

MORITA: I agree. For example, Dr Norman Cousins (1915-1990), who was

---

2. *The Writings of Nichiren Daishonin*, Soka Gakkai, 1999.

called the 'conscience of America' and with whom you have published a dialogue[3], was also a pioneer in research on the medical relationship of the mind and the body.

The Secret Weapon of Hope

PRESIDENT IKEDA: Dr Cousins lived a life of continual challenge and eternal youth. His research into the oneness of mind and body was not simply theoretical, either. He himself achieved miraculous recoveries from collagen illness — a life threatening connective tissue disease — with which he was diagnosed at fifty, and a major heart attack at sixty-five, going on to live until the age of seventy-five. In those years, he produced an enormous amount of work of great and lasting value.

TOYOFUKU: He had a very strong life force. I find his example quite moving.

PRESIDENT IKEDA: The question is, what had so strengthened his life force? I can not help but conclude that it was his love for people and a strong sense of responsibility. Both of those are based on a great faith in humanity. Dr Cousins summed up his beliefs in the single word, *hope.*

Hope, he said, was his secret weapon. In our dialogue, he remarked: "Death is not the greatest tragedy that befalls us in life. What is far more tragic is for an important part of oneself to die while one is still alive. There is no more terrifying tragedy than this. What is important is to accomplish something in this life.[4]

Health is not simply a matter of absence of illness. Health means constant challenge. Constant creativity. A prolific life always moving forward, opening up fresh new vistas — that is a life of true health. An unbeatable spirit is what supplies the power to keep pressing ahead.

MORITA: I am reminded of the story of 'Granny T', who will turn one hundred and two this year. She lives in Kanagawa. She joined the Soka Gakkai when she was sixty-two. She has always been a cheerful, positive and uncomplain-

---

3. Daisaku Ikeda and Norman Cousins, *Sekai Shimin no Taiwa* (Dialogue between World Citizens) (Tokyo, Mainichi Shimbunsha, 1991). Currently published only in Japanese.
4. Translated from Japanese: Daisaku Ikeda, *Watashi no Koyuroku* (Intimate Talks with Global Pioneers) (Tokyo: Yomiuri Shimbunsha, 1996), pg 20.

ing person. While fully involved in Soka Gakkai activities, she conquered the ill health that had long afflicted her, including rheumatism and a heart attack, and she expressed her joy in life in a poem:

Reaching my hundredth year,
My life is blessed
With the merits
Of faithfully practising
The Buddha's teachings.

She also wrote:

In the final chapter
Of my life,
I became a narrator
Of all
That I have seen and done.

She calls herself a 'narrator' partly because four years ago she began giving lectures as an honorary lecturer at a certain technical school, sharing her century of wisdom and experience with many young students.

President Ikeda: She has indeed lived a wonderfully healthy life. Working enthusiastically for others is a wonderful thing, and the members of the Taho-kai (Many Treasures Group), the early pioneers of our movement, are leading the way towards a century of health and a society where all enjoy long and productive lives.

Faith Means Taking Special Care of Your Health

Morita: There is one question that I would like to ask you, President Ikeda, in our first instalment.

President Ikeda: Please do.

Morita: How should we view the relationship between the Buddhist perspective and the medical perspective towards health?

PRESIDENT IKEDA: Yes. People may think they understand this, but they actually often simply jump to some whimsical conclusion and end up getting the relationship between the two totally confused.

TOYOFUKU: I have even heard people say that they are embarrassed to visit a hospital, because that might mean their faith is not strong enough to overcome illness.

MORITA: Thank goodness we do not see as much of that as we used to.

PRESIDENT IKEDA: Indeed. Remember, people do not exist for the sake of religion; religion exists for people's sake. And, Buddhism is based on reason. It is only natural to use every medical means, in the most

> **Health is not simply a matter of absence of illness. Health means constant challenge, constant creativity. A prolific life always moving forward, opening up fresh new vistas — that is a life of true health. An unbeatable spirit is what supplies the power to keep pressing ahead.**

valuable way, to protect our health. It is a mistake to think that we will never fall ill simply because we have faith; to do so is actually a kind of arrogance.

When we have some sort of troubling symptom, it is only right and natural to visit our doctor. In fact, precisely because we are practising faith, we should pay special attention to our health. As Nichiren Daishonin writes, "If you live even one day longer, you can accumulate that much more good fortune. How precious life is!" (*MW*-I-231) And, as we accumulate more good fortune, we are better able to protect Buddhism. The basic reason that I started this new series is that I want to send a message to our dedicated fellow members to live long and healthy lives.

MORITA: We both deeply appreciate your sincere concern for the members' welfare.

The Doctor Aids the Patient's Inherent Healing Powers

PRESIDENT IKEDA: Soka Gakkai 2nd president Josei Toda once said that there are two fundamental problems with people today. One is the confusion of knowledge with wisdom, and the other is the confusion of sickness with death.

Knowledge and wisdom are not the same thing. There is much that can be said about the relationship between the two. With regard to Buddhism and medical science, we can say, very generally, that medicine fights illness with scientific knowledge. Buddhism, on the other hand, develops human wisdom, so that we may find our own rhythm and strengthen our life force. This assists the efficacy of medical treatment and also helps us conquer illness through our own natural healing powers.

MORITA: Wisdom is very important. Certainly, not all doctors lead healthy, long lives. Even today, there are doctors who neglect their health.

TOYOFUKU: The patient's will to live is the driving force behind overcoming illness. This is what we call 'natural healing powers' in medicine. We commonly find that the very same medical treatment has different results depending upon the person's life force, his or her will to live.

MORITA: Life force is a marvellous thing that transcends the realm of human understanding. I suppose that is the meaning of the Western proverb, "The doctor dresses the wound and God heals it."

PRESIDENT IKEDA: I know of another proverb: "God heals, and the doctor takes the fee."

But seriously, it is foolish to ignore or deny the contribution of medicine. Otherwise, faith descends into fanaticism. We must use medical resources wisely in fighting illness. Buddhism gives us the wisdom to use medicine properly.

Wisdom is the basic ingredient to health, to long life, and to happiness. The new century of health, then, must be a new century of wisdom.

Incidentally, Mr Toda also observed that the old Japanese saying, "Good at being sick, but bad at dying," contained an important truth. It is funny how people who are chronically ill seem to live such a long time.

TOYOFUKU: Yes, there are people like that, aren't there? On the other hand, there are those who seem very healthy but are suddenly taken by death in an unforeseen illness or accident. There are also those who feel driven to seek their own death.

PRESIDENT IKEDA: Sickness does not necessarily lead to death. Nichiren

Daishonin writes, "Illness gives rise to the resolve to attain the way." (WND, pg 937) Sickness can force us to examine ourselves, our existence and our lives. It can be a very important and precious motivator. Someone has said that a person who has never been ill only understands half of life.

Morita: I think it was the Swiss philosopher, Carl Hilty (1833-1909), who made the observation that illness cultivates the heart, deepening and broadening it.

Hilty writes: "Just as the flooding river stirs the soil and enriches the fields, sickness stirs and enriches all people's hearts. One who truly understands illness and endures it is made deeper, stronger and greater, and grasps ideas and beliefs that were incomprehensible before."[5]

President Ikeda: The struggle with illness leads us to understand human life fully and forges in us an indomitable spirit. I myself suffered from a weak constitution from the time I was a child. I had tuberculosis and, for that and other reasons, I was not expected to live past thirty.

But that experience helped me understand others who are ill. And, that is why every single moment is so valuable to me, why I have determined to accomplish what I can while I am alive without wasting a minute, and why I have lived full-out all these years.

Toyofuku: Perhaps we can even say that for those who have faith, sickness is the key to real health of spirit and mind.

President Ikeda: Yes. There are many whose bodies are healthy but whose inner being is ill. And, there are also those who suffer some physical disease but whose inner life force is very healthy. All of us will experience some sickness during our lives. That is why it is important to acquire the wisdom to deal with illness properly.

Though it may seem contradictory, from the Buddhist perspective, health and illness are not separate. Nor are life and death. They are part of a single whole. For that reason, the Buddhist perspective on health is not limited to

---

5. Translated from Japanese. Carl Hilty, 'Fuko ni Okeru Kofuku' (Glück im Unglück; Happiness in Unhappiness), *Hiruti Chosakushu* (The Collected Works of Hilty) (Tokyo: Hakusuisha, 1959), vol VII, pg 70.

this single life. Its basic focus is a healthy life throughout the three existences of past, present and future.

For example, even after we enter the phase of death, our life itself persists in a tranquil, latent state, waiting for a new opportunity to continue its mission. When that opportunity arises, it enters the phase of life again and is reborn. We shine with an eternally healthy life throughout all times. In that sense, ultimately we are striving for good health, both in life and in death.

Prevention of Cold and the Harmony of Body and Mind

Participants in this discussion on

' Humanism and the Art of Medicine:

A New Century of Health'

are SGI President Ikeda, Soka Gakkai

Doctors' Division Leaders Dr Shuhei Morita

and Dr Hiroyuki Toyofuku

PRESIDENT IKEDA: Spring weather is so changeable, isn't it?

MORITA: Just when you think it is warm, it suddenly turns cold . . .

PRESIDENT IKEDA: It is easy to get sick in spring — especially, in catching a cold. I hope all our readers will take extra care of their health during this season.

Let us talk about colds in this instalment.

TOYOFUKU: Yes, let's. Almost everyone suffers from colds, no matter what their age or sex.

PRESIDENT IKEDA: It is a universal human illness, the common disease of 5.7 billion.

TOYOFUKU: In Japan, people catch an average of six colds per year.

PRESIDENT IKEDA: Are colds really that common? Does anyone ever die from a cold?

MORITA: Yes, there are cases in which a cold is the direct cause of death. But more often a cold progresses to pneumonia or bronchitis, which is much more life threatening than the common cold. In Japan, pneumonia and bronchitis are the fourth leading cause of death — after cancer, heart disease and stroke — among adults. The elderly, in particular, are at risk and must take special care.

PRESIDENT IKEDA: We should not look on colds lightly, then?

TOYOFUKU: No indeed. Colds can also complicate and worsen the effects of other illnesses, such as heart disease and diabetes.

MORITA: From long ago, colds have been looked upon as the root of a thousand other illnesses. When did people first begin to recognise this fact, I wonder?

PRESIDENT IKEDA: I see — so doctors do not know everything after all! I recall that an ancient Chinese medical text dating back more than two millennia contained the observation that a cold is the chief cause of a hundred illnesses, because it can develop into other illnesses.[1]

Editor's Note: The Japanese term for 'cold', kaze, is both derived from, and has the same pronunciation as, the Japanese word for 'wind'.

A modern, interpretive English translation of the original Chinese text to which President Ikeda refers, reads: "You see that the wind is the cause of many illnesses. Once it penetrates the body, its nature is dynamic and changeable, and has many pathological manifestations. But the cause is always the same: pathogenic wind attacking the body.[2]

TOYOFUKU: That is true. Since we often tend to catch colds when we are run down — due to lack of sleep or leading an unbalanced lifestyle — we are more susceptible to other illnesses, as well, when we have a cold.

PRESIDENT IKEDA: Since colds are 'the root' of many other illnesses, one of the best ways to protect ourselves from other illnesses is to make sure we do not catch a cold. But although we use the single word, *cold*, there are many different types of cold, right?

Many Illnesses can Cause 'Cold Symptoms'

TOYOFUKU: Yes. We use the term *cold* to describe the illness that causes such symptoms as sneezing, a runny nose and fever. These are what are known in medicine as 'cold symptoms'. As long as these symptoms are present, we can call it a cold, no matter what the actual illness might be. As you can see, this is very convenient for us doctors. Of course, we still try to find the real cause of the patient's ailment . . .

PRESIDENT IKEDA: I guess, we'd all better be on the alert the next time our doctor diagnoses us with a cold!

But seriously, it is dangerous to simply dismiss an illness as a cold when you do not have any proper medical knowledge. Nichiren Daishonin writes,

---

1. From the *Huangdi neijing suwen* (The Yellow Emperor's Classic of Medicine). Historians are divided over when this work was written. Some date it in the third millennium BC, while others, the 3rd century BC.
2. *The Yellow Emperor's Classic of Medicine: A New Translation of the Neijing Suwen with Commentary*, trans Maoshing Ni (Boston: Shambhala Publications, Inc, 1995), pg 158.

"If you try to treat someone's illness without knowing its cause of the illness is, you will only make the person sicker than before." (*WND*, pg 774)

By the way, does one catch cold because the weather is cold? There are also summer colds, aren't there?

TOYOFUKU: A person does not catch a cold simply because the weather or temperature is cold.

PRESIDENT IKEDA: I have heard that the scientists who spent the winter at Japan's major research base in the Antarctica, Showa Station, did not catch colds. Is that because they were isolated from others and there were no chance for them to be infected by virus?

TOYOFUKU: Probably. Colds are caused by such things as viruses, mycoplasma, or bacteria. The varieties of these disease organism vary slightly from winter to summer, but they are present and infectious all the year round.

MORITA: Influenza spreads during the winter. Influenza viruses are most active in cold, dry conditions. Our homes in winter are closed up and that also increases our susceptibility. Our throat and nose membranes are also dry, and our resistance is low. Perhaps the best way to think of it is that cold temperatures create the conditions that make it easier to catch a cold.

PRESIDENT IKEDA: What about summer colds? Are they caused by viruses that flourish in summer?

TOYOFUKU: Yes. Adenoviruses, for example, are most active in a humid environment. About eighty per cent of colds are caused by viruses, of which there are more than two hundred varieties. We can identify the virus through laboratory tests, but usually by the time we get the results the patient has recovered from the cold.

MORITA: That is why we usually just leave things at, "It's a cold."

In addition, there is at present no way to cure a cold, even if we know which virus is causing it.

PRESIDENT IKEDA: When I was engaged in a dialogue with Dr Aleksei Khokhlov, professor of physics at Moscow State University and son of the late Dr Rem

Khokhlov, rector of that same university, he told me that viruses are a type of polymer. What does the word, *virus,* mean?

TOYOFUKU: *Virus* is Latin for poison. When viruses were first identified [in 1892], they were thought to be the poisonous matter of bacteria. Later, it was learnt that they were, in fact, a form of matter with genetic material at their core, and that they increased by invading the cells of plants and animals.

PRESIDENT IKEDA: They are your standard villain then, aren't they? They do not have the power to increase on their own, but can only increase their numbers by invading the cells of other living beings!

Can they be seen with a microscope?

MORITA: Yes, viruses can be detected with an electron microscope. They are smaller than bacteria, at most one ten thousandth of a millimetre.

If Catch a Cold

1. **Get plenty of rest.**
2. **Stay warm (maintain the warmth of the body).**
3. **Take plenty of liquids.**
4. **Eat nutritious foods.**

TOYOFUKU: Not all colds are caused by viruses. Part of the cause also lies with the individual. Some people catch colds and some do not, even though they are exposed to the same conditions.

The Disharmony of the Four Elements

PRESIDENT IKEDA: Buddhism speaks of the harmony of the four elements. The ancient Indians viewed life as consisting of the four elements: earth, water, fire and wind. In terms of the body, the bones, hair, teeth and muscles were all regarded as components of earth. The blood and other bodily fluids were water. Body temperature was fire. Breath was wind. All of these elements combined together harmoniously to form the individual human being. Illnesses of the body were regarded as an imbalance or disharmony among these elements.[3]

---

3. According to T'ien-t'ai's *Maka Shikan* (Great Concentration and Insight). For reference, see *WND*, pg 631 [*MW*-II-213 (2nd ed) [248 (1st ed)], *On Curing Karmic Disease.*

MORITA: Medically speaking, 'disharmony of the four elements' — an imbalance in the health of our bodies — leads to a lowered resistance, or a weakening of the immune system. This is what allows a virus to infect us, causing us to catch a cold.

TOYOFUKU: Our resistance to illness can be lowered for many reasons but, in the case of colds, the most likely causes are things, such as getting chilled after a hot bath or from taking a nap without keeping warm, or from overwork.

PRESIDENT IKEDA: It is really important not to let exhaustion accumulate. Avoiding chronic fatigue is the best way to prevent all illnesses. When you are tired, you should go to bed early and get some sleep. Ideally, you should try to shed each day's tiredness within that day. This is all part of the struggle to stay healthy. We must be careful to distinguish between strong faith and overdoing it. When you push yourself too hard, you cannot keep going for long.

Washing your hands and gargling are also important measures for preventing colds, aren't they?

MORITA: Yes. Cold viruses are spread when people sneeze or cough. We breathe the viruses in or carry them from our hands to our mouth and get infected, so we should carefully wash our hands and gargle.

TOYOFUKU: Cold *masks*[4] also prevent us from breathing dust and keep the throat warm and damp, which is effective in preventing infection. Another way you can prevent a cold is to stay away from crowds. Of course, that means that you cannot go to work, go out shopping or attend meetings — making it nigh on impossible to lead a normal life — so, that is pretty much out of the question.

MORITA: Yes, that would be rather tough. All you can really do is strengthen your resistance to colds . . .

TOYOFUKU: When colds are rampant, the place you are most likely to encounter the cold virus is at the doctor's clinic or the hospital. Yet, that does not mean all of the doctors and nurses there are going to catch colds.

---

4. Gauze masks worn over the nose and mouth.

PRESIDENT IKEDA: I see. Building up our resistance is vital, then.

I understand that rubbing down the body with a dry towel or with a cold, wet towel is effective in preventing colds.

MORITA: When you stimulate the skin, the body tenses and the autonomous nervous system is stimulated, raising the body's resistance to illness. The same is true of a cold towel rub. It is only effective even if carried out on exposed parts of the body, such as the wrists or the nape of the neck. Washing your face and hand in cold water is also beneficial.

TOYOFUKU: I once asked some of the members of the Taho-kai (Many Treasures Group), who pioneered our organisation and remain to this day so energetic and high-spirited, what they specifically pay attention to so as to stay in good health. Among the things they listed was "not to catch a cold."

PRESIDENT IKEDA: Paying conscious attention to such things on a daily basis can make a big difference. While a dry towel rub-down physically stimulates the body through the skin, the determination not to catch a cold — coming as it does from the mental and spiritual dimension — stimulates the nerves throughout the body and increases resistance to illness. Once the mind is set in motion, both the brain and the body begin to move to carry out its commands.

MORITA: Speaking of colds, I am reminded of a scene I will never forget. This was during the 2nd World Peace Cultural Festival [held at the Seibu Lions Baseball Stadium in Saitama Prefecture in September 1982]. From before the festival began, it had been raining incessantly. You, President Ikeda, were walking around the stadium ground in the rain, encouraging the participants. One of the guests who was sitting in the stands saw this and wondered what you were saying to them, he later told me. He said he thought you were probably telling them not to let the rain get them down, and to give a good performance in spite of it.

But when you came around to the section where he was sitting, you said through a hand microphone, "Thank you all for being here. Please take care not to catch a cold in this rain." When he heard those words delivered, with your voice full of concern for the members, he was really moved, he said, and he felt that this was how a true leader should be.

PRESIDENT IKEDA: I only did what anyone would do . . . The health of our members is my number one priority. My dearest wish is that all can be healthy and energetic so that they can participate fully in society. I am always praying for the members' health.

'The Evil Influence of the Wind'

MORITA: I wonder why the word for a common cold in Japanese, *kaze*, is written with the Chinese characters meaning 'the evil influence of the wind'

PRESIDENT IKEDA: In ancient Chinese texts, 'external air' was thought to be transformed into 'negative energy' that caused disease, so it was referred to as 'the wind's evil influence'.

MORITA: I wonder if Nichiren Daishonin caught colds?

TOYOFUKU: I do not know whether he himself ever caught one, but we do find the names of illnesses that are thought to correspond to the common cold in Kamakura-period records. They are somewhat similar to the modern Japanese term for 'cold', *kaze*, and contain the 'wind' (*kaze*) element, as well — for example, *kazehiki* or *kazeke*.

PRESIDENT IKEDA: We find the word *kazeke* (chill or cold) in the *Gosho*, in a passage describing how Ryokan of Gokuraku-ji temple pretended to be ill so as to avoid having to engage in a public debate with Nichiren Daishonin who had then returned to Kamakura from his exile on Sado Island.

In the Gosho, The Teaching, Practice and Proof, *the Daishonin recalls: "When I actually did return to Kamakura, Ryokan shut his gates and forbade anyone to enter. At times, he even feigned illness, saying that he had caught a cold [kazeke]." (WND, pg 482)*

They say that whoever discovers a cure for the common cold is bound to win a Nobel Prize. Is there any particular medicine that works?

MORITA: Unfortunately, it does not seem like we will see anyone win that Nobel Prize soon.

PRESIDENT IKEDA: What about the medication one receives from the doctor or that is available over-the-counter?

TOYOFUKU: The medication presently available does not do anything to cure the actual cause of a cold. What it does is relieve cold symptoms, such as headaches, fever, runny nose, coughing and sneezing.

MORITA: The basic treatment for a cold is to stay warm, eat nutritious food, take plenty of liquids and generally leave it up to your body's own natural recuperative powers to get well, while using medicine to help alleviate the cold symptoms.

PRESIDENT IKEDA: It is important to get plenty of rest when you are ill. But that can be difficult for us with our busy modern lives, can't it?

TOYOFUKU: Overexerting yourself only leads to accidents. When you catch a cold, you should endeavour to get plenty of rest. If that is not possible, you should at least keep warm and eat nutritious foods.

PREVENTION OF COLD

1. **The determination not to catch a cold.**
2. **Washing your hands and gargling.**
3. **Shed each day's tiredness within that day.**
4. **Rubbing down the body with a dry towel or with a cold-wet towel is effective.**

A Fever is Part of the Body's Self-defence

PRESIDENT IKEDA: Why does a fever often accompany a cold?

TOYOFUKU: A fever is part of the body's defence mechanism as it attempts to cure the cold quickly. When the body's temperature rises, the activity of the virus is slowed.

PRESIDENT IKEDA: We are told to drink plenty of fluids when we have a cold or fever. Is it all right to drink tea as part of those fluids?

TOYOFUKU: Green tea and black tea both contain a substance called catechin,

A wise and judicious lifestyle brimming with vitality, in which the four elements are kept in balance and the harmony of body and mind are preserved, is the best way to both prevent and treat a cold.

which is said to be effective in inhibiting the spread of the virus.

PRESIDENT IKEDA: Some seem to prefer to take those extra liquids in the form of alcoholic refreshments.

TOYOFUKU: Actually, it is a bad idea to drink alcohol when you have got a cold because alcohol dehydrates you. It causes you to release more water than you take in when you drink it.

MORITA: You should never drink alcohol when you are taking any kind of medicine. It may intensify the effects of the medicine or cause other negative side effects.

PRESIDENT IKEDA: What about baths?

TOYOFUKU: It is usually not a good idea to take a bath when you have a fever, because baths can put a drain on your energy and there is also the possibility of being chilled after your bath.

PRESIDENT IKEDA: What should we eat when we catch a cold?

MORITA: When you first start to catch a cold, you should take warm soup and stews that will warm you internally. When you start to cough and suffer from sore throat, soft foods that can be easily swallowed are best. When your nose is congested, you should drink soup. The steam will help decongest you.

TOYOFUKU: When you have a fever, you may not have much of an appetite, so you should try to increase your liquid intake with such things as juice, pudding, or even ice cream. If you have severe diarrhoea, however, you should not force yourself to eat. But, because it is easy to become dehydrated when you have a fever or diarrhoea, you must take special care to get plenty of liquid.

PRESIDENT IKEDA: A wise and judicious lifestyle brimming with vitality, in which the four elements are kept in balance and the harmony of body and mind are preserved, is the best way to both prevent and treat a cold.

A Daily Guide in Health Education

Participants in this discussion on
' Humanism and the Art of Medicine:
A New Century of Health'
are SGI President Ikeda, Soka Gakkai
Doctors' Division Leaders Dr Shuhei Morita
and Dr Hiroyuki Toyofuku

Overweight and Obesity

MORITA: We have received many positive responses to our series so far. Along with words of praise, a few of our readers have even written in asking that we give them some advice on how to lose weight!

PRESIDENT IKEDA: Though we may chuckle at that request, weight is actually a serious concern for many people as well as a general barometer of our overall health. Let us make overweight and obesity our topic for today.

MORITA: That is an excellent idea. I am sure many of our readers will be interested in this topic.

TOYOFUKU: Though of course obesity can be a serious problem, I am concerned about the trend for some people, especially those young women who are really not overweight at all, to adopt extreme diets in order to lose weight.

PRESIDENT IKEDA: It is certainly true that many people today are almost obsessed with losing weight. Almost too much emphasis seems to be placed on being thin in our society.

What are the Medical Criteria for Determining if One is Overweight?

TOYOFUKU: A widely used method of calculating 'average weight' in Japan is to square one's height in metres[1] and then multiply the result by 22. For example, I am 161 centimetres (5ft 4in) tall, so I multiply 1.61 by 1.61, and then by 22 (1.61 x 1.61 x 22). This comes to about 57 kilograms (multiply by 2.2 for pounds — in this case, around 126 pounds), which is the average weight for someone my height. You are regarded as overweight if your weight is more than 20 per cent higher than the average weight for a person of that height.

---

1. Approximate metric conversion formula: To convert feet into centimetres multiply by 30, and to convert inches into centimetres multiply by 2.5. And, to convert centimetres into metres divide by 100. (Approximate conversion only.)

Percentage of Body Fat is a Better Measure of Obesity than Body Size

PRESIDENT IKEDA: I know they say that each time you let your belt out by one notch, you are reducing your life span by so many years, but exactly why is it unhealthy to be overweight? Also, is it not important to take differences in people's physical build into account? Although people may appear similarly overweight, some are big-boned, others very muscular, while some have a lot of body fat. Do these differences have any effect on one's health?

TOYOFUKU: Indeed they do. As far as one's health is concerned, it is not so much appearance or physical size as the amount of body fat that is important.

MORITA: When one has too much fat, one is susceptible to a variety of illnesses, including high blood pressure, diabetes, hyperlipemia (the presence of excess fat or lipids in the blood) and heart disease.

TOYOFUKU: Where the fat is located in one's body is also a decisive factor. Recently, the terms 'apple-shaped' obesity and 'pear-shaped' obesity have become widely used in Japan — the former type of obesity referring to excess weight that accumulates around the torso or upper body and the latter to that deposited mainly around the hips and thighs, or the lower part of the body. Men are more inclined towards apple-shaped obesity, while pear-shaped obesity is more common in women.

MORITA: In apple-shaped obesity, fat is deposited around one's internal organs. In pear-shaped obesity, it is mostly beneath the skin layer, or in what is called the subcutaneous tissue. This is very apparent when a CT scan[2] — cross-sectional photograph — is taken of the area around one's navel. Apple-shaped obesity is more likely to lead to excess fat or lipids in the blood and greater susceptibility to a variety of diseases.

---

2. CT: Computed tomography. Radiography in which a three-dimensional image of a body structure is constructed by computer from a series of plane cross-sectional images made along an axis.

PRESIDENT IKEDA: It is often said that these days more and more children are suffering from adult diseases. Is this related to obesity?

TOYOFUKU: Yes, I believe so.

PRESIDENT IKEDA: What, in a nutshell, is the cause of obesity?

TOYOFUKU: The direct cause of obesity is — surprise! — overeating. When we take in more energy than we expend, the excess energy is stored in the body as fat. Naturally, a lack of daily exercise is another cause.

MORITA: We should note, however, that obesity can also be caused by hormone imbalance, so it is important to check with a doctor to properly ascertain the cause of obesity.

Eating Out of Frustration

TOYOFUKU: Stress can also be an important factor in obesity, since some people react to stress by overeating. They try to take their minds off their spiritual or emotional frustrations by eating and drinking, and before they know it they have made a habit of overeating. This is very common.

MORITA: On the opposite end of the spectrum, there are eating disorders, such as anorexia nervosa or bulimia, which are most frequently seen in young women.[3] It is thought that society's equation of thinness with beauty may lie at the root of these disorders.

PRESIDENT IKEDA: In the days when many people did not have enough to eat, a plump figure was regarded as a symbol of good health and affluence. It was the aesthetic ideal and the standard of beauty. In fact, this is still true in many societies around the globe.

TOYOFUKU: Yes, there are regions where being called plump is still thought of as a compliment.

---

3. Anorexia nervosa is characterised by an extreme reduction in food intake, almost to the point of starvation, and bulimia is typified by a cycle of binge-eating followed by self-induced vomiting and purging.

MORITA: Such an ideal is only natural when one considers that much of human history has been a battle against starvation. The ability of the body to store excess energy as fat was very useful in such circumstances. In addition, the layer of subcutaneous fat on women's lower abdomens also serves as protection during pregnancy, absorbing shocks and jolts that might otherwise harm the foetus.

PRESIDENT IKEDA: The mechanism for storing excess energy as fat is the body's ingenious way of preserving life in difficult times. But our circumstances and lifestyles have now changed greatly. Japan, too, has entered an age of excess, and accompanying overconsumption of food is steadily undermining people's health. While our bodies grow more corpulent, our minds and spirits are wasting away from starvation.

Incidentally, we often hear of people with such high metabolisms that they can eat whatever they want without gaining weight, making them the envy of those who put on weight easily. Is this a hereditary condition?

WHY OVERWEIGHT?

1. **Over-eating.**
2. **Indisciplined eating habit.**
3. **Imbalance diet.**
4. **Lack of daily exercise.**
5. **React to stress and may be due to hormone imbalance (sickness).**

Daily Habits Play a Bigger Role than Heredity

MORITA: We believe that people do inherit a tendency to become overweight. But that tendency does not condemn them to actually becoming overweight. What really matters are the habits one acquires from early childhood, particularly with regard to exercise and eating.

TOYOFUKU: Obesity harms not only the internal organs. Excess body fat is an extra load that we have to carry around with us. It exerts pressure on the back and the knees, and makes them susceptible to damage. Obesity also strains the heart and lungs — think of the way an overweight person puffs when he climbs a flight of stairs.

Sakyamuni also Cautioned against Overeating

PRESIDENT IKEDA: Yes, there was a king like that among Sakyamuni's disciples of whom the following episode appears in the Buddhist scriptures. King Prasenajit (Pali: Pasenadi) of the kingdom of Kosala came to visit the Buddha. He was heavily overweight, and when he appeared before the Buddha he was puffing and panting from the exertion of his journey. The king was a prodigious eater, and he had just finished a huge meal before setting out. Sakyamuni looked at him with a compassionate smile:

> Those who are ever mindful,
> Observing moderation in what they eat,
> Will suffer little and age slowly,
> Thus prolonging their life.[4]

King Prasenajit turned to the young prince, Sudassana, standing behind him at the time, and asked him to memorise Sakyamuni's teaching and whisper it in his ear at every meal, promising to reward the prince for this service. Sudassana did as he was requested, and the king, hearing Sakyamuni's verse each time he sat down to a meal, gradually stopped overeating and became trim and healthy.

TOYOFUKU: Guarding against overeating so that one can remain youthful and enjoy a long and healthy life is the very soundest of medical advice.

Stop before You are Full

PRESIDENT IKEDA: Now, I would like to ask for your practical suggestions as doctors for losing and keeping off excess weight. I know this is what interests our readers most!

MORITA: Certainly. Our readers will have to understand, however, that there aren't any miracle cures for losing weight overnight. First, as far as meal-

---

4. *Budda: Kamigami to no Taiwa — San'yutta-Nikaya I,* trans Hajime Nakamura (Tokyo: Iwanami Shoten, 1986), pg 182. cf *The Book of Kindred Sayings (Sanyutta-Nikaya)* Part I; *Kindred Sayings with Verses (Sagatha-Vagga),* trans Mrs Rhys Davids (Oxford: Pali Text Society, 1993), pg 124.

Some people complain that they cannot lose weight no matter how much they restrict their food intake, but often they do not pay careful attention to what they eat or drink apart from meals — for example, fruit for dessert or a snack at mid-day, or the alcoholic beverages they drink.

times are concerned, the most basic rule is to eat only so much as to feel 'eight-tenth full', as we say in Japanese. In other words, to leave some room to spare.

Toyofuku: Yes, one should stop eating just at the point when one wants to eat just a little more. Of course, that requires a lot of discipline. But if you can do that, you will be surprised at the difference it makes.

Morita: Some people complain that they can not lose weight no matter how much they restrict their food intake, but often they do not pay careful attention to what they eat or drink apart from meals — for example, fruit for dessert or a snack at midday, or the alcoholic beverages they drink. All of those calories need to be counted as well.

President Ikeda: What about eating late at night?

Morita: Like eating between meals during the day, it is best to avoid late-night snacking. You do not use much energy at night, and whatever calories you take in are more likely to be stored as fat.

Toyofuku: An unbalanced diet also contributes to obesity. So, we must pay careful attention not only to how much we eat but what we eat. It is crucial to consume a wide variety of nutritious food so that our body can get all the vitamins and minerals it needs, but at the sametime, do not take in more calories than we are likely to expend.

'Eat with Your Head'

MORITA: The basics of a healthy weight-control diet are to eat three regular and balanced meals. Skipping breakfast or making your evening meal the biggest meal of the day is to be avoided.

PRESIDENT IKEDA: Easier said than done, as the saying goes.

TOYOFUKU: Yes, but if dieters stray from this regimen and go back to skipping meals and eating large meals late at night, they may soon find that their waistline is even bigger than before they started trying to reduce their weight!

There are some practical tips we can use to stay trim and healthy, though. For example, do not eat too quickly. Eat slowly and pay attention to what you are eating. You will find that if you do that, you will feel full with a smaller amount of food. Another helpful hint is to eat plenty of vegetables first, which will satisfy much of your hunger.

PRESIDENT IKEDA: I see. As the saying goes, "Eat with your head, not with your mouth." In other words, we have to eat with wisdom and discernment.

How can we improve our diet? How can we control our desire to eat more than we need? How do we discipline ourselves? How we grapple with these challenges is a sign of our character and wisdom.

TOYOFUKU: Yes. In the past, you have spoken about sound eating habits as one of the criteria for staying healthy. The English word *diet* can also refer to a governing body of elected representatives, but its original meaning was 'policy' or 'plan'.

PRESIDENT IKEDA: Perhaps we can say that the essential meaning of the term *diet* is a wise policy for living.

MORITA: If we ignore that truth and adopt some radical food regimen, we can fall victim to anaemia, hair loss, or other symptoms. Poor diet can even affect the heart. Instead of gaining the healthy slenderness we had hoped for, a radically restricted diet is more likely to lead to an unhealthy pallor and gauntness.

PRESIDENT IKEDA: Rather than worrying about how you appear to others, the important thing is whether you can control your own life and be satisfied with yourself. That kind of balanced and intelligent life is what we might call a true 'diet'.

What it comes down to, basically, is whether or not you have a solid sense of purpose in life.

Brisk Walking and Calisthenics are Effective in Weight Loss

PRESIDENT IKEDA: Exercise is also an indispensable element in losing weight, isn't it?

OVERCOMING OBESITY

1. **Eat only 'eight-tenth full'.**
2. **Eat slowly.**
3. **Eat three regular and balanced meals.**
4. **Avoid eating between meals and avoid late-night snacking.**
5. **Proper exercise.**

TOYOFUKU: It certainly is. Proper exercise is very important. When exercised, muscles increase in strength and size. When one tries to lose weight by dieting alone, it is actually muscle tissue that the body starts to burn before using up its fat stores, and this can be detrimental to one's health.

PRESIDENT IKEDA: What kind of exercise aren't really suited to weight loss then?

MORITA: Many competitive sports — particularly those that require short bursts of enormous energy, such as the dash — burn glycogen and other materials before they burn fat. As a result, they are not really effective in losing weight. The best exercise is the kind that involves the whole body, allowing one to breathe deeply, warm up slowly, and use all the major muscle groups.

TOYOFUKU: Practical suggestions for exercise might be brisk walking or calisthenics. The important thing is to exercise for a certain period of time each day, moving the entire body and taking in plenty of oxygen. That is how the body is encouraged to burn fat.

The Milkman is Healthier than
Those Who Drink the Milk

MORITA: I have a Men's Division acquaintance who began delivering the *Seikyo Shimbun*, the Soka Gakkai newspaper, many years ago, partly for the sake of his health, and who continues to do so to this day.[5] When he started, he was a little overweight, but after waking up early and getting a moderate amount of exercise everyday, he soon lost the weight and became much firmer and trimmer all over. He proudly told me that, at his most recent check-up, the doctor had given him a clean bill of health, proclaiming him to be the very picture of good health and possessing the physique of a person ten years younger.

PRESIDENT IKEDA: That is wonderful. His efforts are truly admirable. I pray for his safety and longevity. In the West, there is a saying, "The milkman is healthier than those who drink the milk he delivers."

Not only in your friend's physical well-being, but in his desire to transmit Nichiren Daishonin's Buddhism to others and work for people's happiness, I think we can discern the true essence of good health.

Mahatma Gandhi believed that we should eat only to live so that we may be of service to our fellow human beings, not for the sake of indulging ourselves.[6]

The desire to serve others and to live long and healthy lives so that we can achieve this is more important, I feel, than our external appearance, whether we think we are fat or thin. And that, I believe, is the meaning of a healthy diet from the Buddhist perspective.

---

5. In Japan, the *Seikyo Shimbun* is delivered by Soka Gakkai members who volunteer to take on this responsibility. Each morning they deliver the papers door-to-door to subscribers in their local neighbourhood areas, either by bicycle or on foot, or, in areas that are very spread out, by motorcycle.
6. Mahatma Gandhi, *The Health Guide* (New York: The Crossing Press, 1978), pg 188.

Blood Pressure

Participants in this discussion on
' Humanism and the Art of Medicine:
A New Century of Health'
are SGI President Ikeda, Soka Gakkai
Doctors' Division Leaders Dr Shuhei Morita
and Dr Hiroyuki Toyofuku

PRESIDENT IKEDA: Let us discuss blood pressure today.

MORITA: All right. Everyone seems to think they know what blood pressure is, but many actually have a surprising lack of accurate knowledge on the subject.

PRESIDENT IKEDA: I always wonder what doctors are listening to with their stethoscope when checking a person's blood pressure.

TOYOFUKU: They are listening to what are called 'Korotkov sounds'.

PRESIDENT IKEDA: And, those sounds help them measure blood pressure?

TOYOFUKU: When we measure a patient's blood pressure, we first temporarily stop the circulation of blood in the patient's arm by pumping air into the cuff (of the sphygmomanometer, the piece of equipment used to measure blood pressure) and thereby constricting the normal blood flow. We then place our stethoscope on an artery located on the inner side of the elbow joint, and, as we slowly decrease the pressure in the cuff by gradually letting out the air, we can begin to hear vibrations — the sound of blood rushing back into the arm in rhythm with the heartbeat. This sound is like an announcement that the blood has started flowing again. What is measured at this time is the highest (systolic) blood pressure.

PRESIDENT IKEDA: That is the upper number in the fraction used to indicate blood pressure, isn't it?

MORITA: Yes. This is the blood pressure at the moment when the heart contracts and pushes blood strongly through the body, so it is also called systolic blood pressure.

TOYOFUKU: Then, as we continue to lessen the pressure in the cuff, the vibrations disappear. What we measure at that moment when we can no longer hear the sound is the lowest, or diastolic, blood pressure — the lower number of the blood pressure fraction. It is called diastolic because it is the blood pressure at the time when the heart relaxes.

PRESIDENT IKEDA: I see. I suppose these vibrations are called 'Korotkov sounds' after their discoverer?

TOYOFUKU: Yes, this method of measuring blood pressure by means of a stethoscope was first thought of by Nikolai Korotkov, a Russian surgeon, in 1905.

PRESIDENT IKEDA: What is blood pressure, exactly?

MORITA: It is the force exerted against the walls of the arteries by the flow of blood being pumped from the heart.

TOYOFUKU: The body is said to contain some sixty trillion[1] cells. To support the activities of all those cells, an intricate web of blood vessels covers every inch of our body. The heart must, therefore, pump blood, a relatively viscous substance, with considerable force through this vast network.

PRESIDENT IKEDA: Blood pressure also changes with a person's age, doesn't it?

MORITA: From youth to adulthood, it increases at a regular pace, but after that it stabilises. Then, from about middle age, the walls of our blood vessels start to lose their resilience and begin to harden. As a result, the heart must pump harder to push blood to every corner of the body.

PRESIDENT IKEDA: And, that is why our blood pressure rises, right? What are the standards against which blood pressure is judged to be high or low?

TOYOFUKU: Normal blood pressure is considered a systolic (highest) pressure of 139 millimetres of mercury and under a diastolic (lowest) pressure of 89 millimetres and under. High blood pressure is when the systolic pressure is over 160mm or the diastolic pressure is over 90mm. For example, a reading of 136/98mm represents high blood pressure. Low blood pressure is when the systolic pressure is less than 100mm.

PRESIDENT IKEDA: Which is more dangerous, when the systolic or diastolic pressure is too high?

MORITA: Changes in diastolic pressure are usually much smaller than those in systolic pressure, so a marked increase in diastolic blood pressure is more dangerous.

---

1. Sixty trillion: 60^{12}.

PRESIDENT IKEDA: What is the optimal spread between the two rates?

TOYOFUKU: Generally, about 50mm for adults, but there's no need to worry about the precise figure.

PRESIDENT IKEDA: They say blood pressure rises when we get angry. Does blood pressure really change so easily?

MORITA: It changes quite dramatically throughout the course of the day. For example, it is on the high side when we are awake and on the low side when we are sleeping. It also changes throughout the year. It tends to rise from fall through winter, and be lower from spring through summer.

Avoid Sharp Temperature Changes

TOYOFUKU: There are significant differences in our blood pressure, depending upon whether we are resting or active, tense or relaxed. If we get excited, or if we experience a sudden, extreme change in temperature, our blood pressure will soar.

PRESIDENT IKEDA: We should try to avoid such situations, then. One often hears about people collapsing after being in a warm room, and suddenly rushing out into the cold or getting out of a hot bath and being exposed to the cold.

MORITA: Some people with normal blood pressure get tense when they are about to have their blood pressure measured by a white-gowned doctor or nurse and experience an elevation in blood pressure. This is called 'white coat hypertension'.

TOYOFUKU: Yes, and there can be a surprising difference depending upon whether the doctor or the nurse, who is taking the blood pressure, is stern and intimidating-looking or gentle and understanding.

PRESIDENT IKEDA: So, blood pressure reacts in a very human way, then!
    Nowadays, there are simple automated gadgets available in the market that allow you to measure your blood pressure in the convenience of your own home.

MORITA: Yes, and I highly recommend them for people with high blood pressure. Measuring your own blood pressure at home is an excellent way to monitor and control high blood pressure.

PRESIDENT IKEDA: You are saying we should watch our own blood pressure. In other words, if we really wish to protect and preserve our health, we need to be the patient, doctor and nurse, all in one. It won't do, of course, to diagnose and treat ourselves. We should always remember to seek our doctor's advice.

Few Obvious Symptoms

PRESIDENT IKEDA: One of the characteristics of hypertension, or high blood pressure, I hear, is that there are few obvious symptoms to warn us of a problem. Some call it the 'silent killer'.

TOYOFUKU: Yes. Since there are few warning signs of hypertension, we may have it and continue to live in ways that make it worse. But whether we are aware that we have high blood pressure or not, our heart continues to enlarge and our arteries to harden.

MORITA: If we allow hypertension to go untreated, it can lead or contribute to many serious conditions, such as intracerebral haemorrhage, cerebral infarction, coronary heart disease in the form of angina and myocardial infarction, retinal haemorrhage and renal failure.

PRESIDENT IKEDA: What is the cause of high blood pressure?

TOYOFUKU: In some cases, it is caused by problems with the kidneys, the adrenal gland, or the endocrine system. They are the causes of so-called secondary hypertension.

MORITA: This accounts for, at most, ten per cent of hypertension patients. The other ninety per cent — cases of hypertension for which the causes are not really known — fall into the category of primary, or essential, hypertension. But though we do not know the precise causes in these cases, we do have a fairly clear understanding of the factors that cause blood pressure to rise.

Salt, Stress, Obesity and Exhaustion

PRESIDENT IKEDA: What are those factors?

TOYOFUKU: First, there are genetic factors. People can inherit the tendency to have high blood pressure. Then, there are such contributing factors as ageing, high salt intake, high levels of cholesterol, obesity, cold, stress, exhaustion, lack of sleep and excess intake of alcohol.

MORITA: Special note should be made of the link between high blood pressure and stress. It is thought that when we experience stress, our nerves send signals to our heart to increase the pulse, causing blood capillaries to contract and blood pressure to rise.

TOYOFUKU: In general, people living in urban areas have higher blood pressure than those who do not, and when people move from a quieter area to a big city, their blood pressure commonly rises. The crowding and other stressful elements of urban life are probably the cause of the higher level.

The Three Poisons of Greed, Anger and Stupidity Weaken Our Life Force

PRESIDENT IKEDA: From a Buddhist perspective, Nichiren Daishonin writes, "As the poisons of greed, anger and foolishness gradually intensify, the life span of human beings gradually decreases and their stature diminishes." (WND, pg 1120) As greed, anger and stupidity intensify in our lives, our strong and healthy life-force is weakened and diminished. These three poisons create stress and disturb the balance of body and mind, and can even cut short our life span.

MORITA: It is certainly true that hot-tempered people are always tense, resulting in elevated blood pressure.

TOYOFUKU: High blood pressure is closely linked to two of the three leading adult diseases: it is an important factor in heart disease and stroke, though it does not seem to be related to cancer. There are also data indicating that those with high blood pressure do not live as long as others.

PRESIDENT IKEDA: We might think of the three poisons as the 'villains' manipulating the 'silent killer' from behind the scenes, then!

The challenge is how we can learn to control anger and the rest of the three poisons in a constructive way, to wisely redirect cravings and desires arising from the three poisons towards enlightenment. This is the Buddhist principle of transforming earthly desires into enlightenment. Through the resources of compassion, wisdom, courage and hope that we marshal towards this end, we can forge a strong and healthy life force and maintain a sound physical and mental balance.

MORITA: I agree. Even those who are susceptible to hypertension can prevent the occurrence of illness by good management of their physical and mental well-being.

TOYOFUKU: I hope all our readers will have regular check-ups of their blood pressure, and that, if they have an abnormal reading, they will heed the results and follow a wise course of treatment.

CAUSES OF HIGH BLOOD PRESSURE

1. **Genetic factors.**
2. **Excitement or a sudden, extreme change in temperature.**
3. **High salt intake.**
4. **Obesity.**
5. **Stress.**

In our next discussion session, let us examine some treatments for hypertension and also take a look at the problem of low blood pressure.

PRESIDENT IKEDA: This time we are going to talk about treating high blood pressure, aren't we?

MORITA: Yes. Let us start with the most common type of high blood pressure — essential, or primary, hypertension.

TOYOFUKU: We say essential or primary because we do not know the cause of this type of high blood pressure. Since we do not know the cause, there is at present basically no way to cure essential hypertension. With careful and continued treatment, however, blood pressure can be lowered.

Seven Grams of Salt Per Day

PRESIDENT IKEDA: What are the most common treatments?

TOYOFUKU: The first step is to change one's lifestyle. This is a drugless treatment. One important area to change is one's eating habits, especially reducing salt intake and eating a balanced diet.

PRESIDENT IKEDA: Why is salt bad?

MORITA: The main ingredient in salt is sodium, which raises blood pressure. If possible, we should try to restrict the salt in our diet to about seven grams a day.

A level teaspoon of salt is approximately five grams; a teaspoon of soy sauce contains about one gram of salt.

PRESIDENT IKEDA: But many people complain that lightly salted foods do not have enough taste.

TOYOFUKU: There are a few handy tricks that can improve the taste of food without adding salt. For example, one can use reduced-salt soy sauce, or flavour foods with ginger, horseradish or other spices to perk them up without increasing their salt content.

MORITA: Another trick, if one really craves salt, is to use it mainly in just one of the dishes at the meal.

PRESIDENT IKEDA: What are some important nutrients for people suffering from high blood pressure?

MORITA: Potassium is important because it lowers blood pressure. There is a lot of potassium in green or yellow coloured vegetables (ie, vegetables rich in beta-carotene), such as spinach, as well as in bananas and potatoes.

TOYOFUKU: One should also make sure one's diet includes plenty of calcium, fibre and fish, and also vegetable oil.

PRESIDENT IKEDA: Obesity is also a contributing factor in high blood pressure, isn't it?

MORITA: Yes. Simply losing weight will generally lower high blood pressure. It is also important to get some kind of exercise, such as brisk walking, on a daily basis.

TOYOFUKU: One must also be careful not to drink too much alcohol. People with high blood pressure are also advised to give up smoking.

PRESIDENT IKEDA: What can be done when the measures we have mentioned so far do not have any effect?

MORITA: The next step is to try to treat high blood pressure with drugs. The actual degree of high blood pressure is what determines whether drugs may be an effective treatment. But age and other factors also have to be taken into consideration, so it is best to seek the advice of one's physician.

TOYOFUKU: But just because one begins a course of treatment using drugs does not mean one can stop the programme of diet and exercise. That must continue with the drug treatment.

TREATMENT FOR HIGH BLOOD PRESSURE

1. **Reduce/Control salt intake.**
2. **Weight control.**
3. **Brisk walking, on a daily basis.**
4. **Relieve stress.**
5. **Avoid sudden change in temperature.**
6. **Medication.**

PRESIDENT IKEDA: Do the drugs for controlling high blood pressure have to be taken for the rest of one's life?

TOYOFUKU: As a rule, it is a lifelong drug regimen. Anti-hypertension drugs do not treat the actual cause of high blood pressure; they just bring the blood pressure down. If one stops taking the drug, the blood pressure rises again.

But there are certain cases where one can stop taking the drug after a period of time.

PRESIDENT IKEDA: Do such drugs have side effects?

MORITA: Yes, a few. But none are life-threatening. Anyone who is concerned about side effects, however, should confer with their doctor.

PRESIDENT IKEDA: One often hears of people who decide to stop taking their blood pressure medicine without consulting their doctor and then collapse. Sometimes they have a stroke or heart attack.

MORITA: That is true. Many people who have done this have placed themselves in great danger.

PRESIDENT IKEDA: This is important, then. I hope everyone will remember this.

MORITA: In any question concerning increasing or decreasing prescribed medication or stopping it altogether, it is best to follow the recommendation of one's doctor.

TOYOFUKU: Some people actually fib to the doctor, saying that they are taking their medicine as directed when in fact they are not. But this only prevents the doctor from offering appropriate treatment, so it is important to be honest with one's doctor.

PRESIDENT IKEDA: They are obviously trying to create a favourable impression with the doctor, but such pretence is to no purpose. Their own health is at stake, after all.

We Cure Ourselves; Doctors are Our Helpers

MORITA: Yes, the patient's cooperation is very important. With chronic diseases like hypertension that require treatment over an extended period of time, you can not just sit back and hope that the doctor will somehow cure you. The doctor devises a strategy for treatment, but it is the patient who effects the cure — by regular clinic visits, taking the prescribed medicine and following the proper diet.

PRESIDENT IKEDA: A certain Buddhist scripture teaches that those who are ill should take an active and involved approach to their illness by: (1) eating foods and taking medicines beneficial to the recovery from the illness; (2) following the advice of those who are treating and nursing them; (3) having an awareness of whether their illness is serious or mild; (4) bearing suffering bravely; and (5) possessing wisdom and never ceasing to make efforts to get well.[1]

This is not a system of leaving things up to the doctor. It teaches us that we have to play an active part in our own recovery. Just as we said in the previous instalment, each of us is basically our own physician.

TOYOFUKU: Doctors should also strive to ensure that the patient has a fundamental understanding of the nature of his or her illness.

PRESIDENT IKEDA: Yes, I fully agree. Treatment is most effective when the patient works together with a good doctor. For that to happen, there must be a relationship of trust between the doctor and the patient. People aren't machines. The treatment of disease is not like repairing a piece of mechanical equipment. There is ample evidence to show that warm encouragement, and sensitive care and concern can have a truly dramatic positive impact on a patient's recovery.

> **Treatment is most effective when the patient works together with a good doctor. For that to happen, there must be a relationship of trust between the doctor and the patient.**

The Power of One's Voice

PRESIDENT IKEDA: Is there anything else that might be helpful in reducing high blood pressure?

MORITA: Actually, reciting sutras is said to relieve stress and lower blood pressure.

---

1. From the *Makasogi Ritsu* (The Great Canon of Monastic Rules). A work of *vinaya* or rules of discipline of the Mahasamghika school, translated into Chinese by Buddhabhadra and Fa-hsien in 416.

PRESIDENT IKEDA: Really! I cannot wait to tell this to the Men's Division members in particular.

MORITA: Of course, doing gongyo and chanting daimoku increase our life force, but we also know that, medically speaking, sitting up straight and breathing deeply from the stomach, as we do when we chant and recite, is good for us.

TOYOFUKU: When our respiratory system is working well, our blood circulation also improves. Vocalising is also a good way of relieving stress.

PRESIDENT IKEDA: And, there are all kinds of vocalising, aren't there? Some mothers, it seems, give vent to their stress by scolding their children!

The best way to chant is neither too loud nor too soft, but in a clear and invigorating voice, and with the rhythm of a galloping horse. Since we ourselves embody the Law of life, Nam-myoho-renge-kyo, we should chant our *daimoku* with an open and relaxed frame of mind with the intention of thoroughly tuning our own life's inner rhythm.

MORITA: Another thing people with high blood pressure should avoid, as we mentioned in the previous instalment, is sudden changes in temperature.

PRESIDENT IKEDA: The elderly, in particular, often collapse after a hot bath or shower, or when they get up from a warm bed in the middle of the night to go to the toilet, or after going out suddenly from a warm house into the cold outdoors.

TOYOFUKU: That happens because the sympathetic nervous system suddenly tenses, causing the capillaries and smaller blood vessels to contract, which in turn triggers an abrupt rise in blood pressure.

PRESIDENT IKEDA: One way to avoid that would be to get dressed in a warm room straight after having had a hot bath or shower and thus preventing exposure to a sudden change in temperature.

MORITA: Yes. It is also a good idea to ensure that the bathroom is kept warm.

PRESIDENT IKEDA: When one has to go out into the cold, it is important to be mentally prepared, consciously registering, "I'm heading out into the cold now." That allows the body to prepare for the cold. It can be dangerous to just rush outside without thinking.

TOYOFUKU: Now that many buildings are air-conditioned, there is also a large gap in the indoor and outdoor temperatures even in the summer. It is important to put on sufficient clothing in a strongly air-conditioned room in order to keep warm and not catch a chill.

Low Blood Pressure

PRESIDENT IKEDA: Buddhism teaches us: "The wise may be called human, but the thoughtless are no more than animals." (*WND*, pg 852) If we are wise, we can prevent accidents before they happen.

By the way, some people suffer from low blood pressure, or hypotension, don't they?

TOYOFUKU: Yes, indeed. We often hear people say that they have a hard time getting up in the morning because of their low blood pressure.

MORITA: Medically speaking, however, we cannot say that having low blood pressure necessarily means one will have a hard time getting up in the morning.

PRESIDENT IKEDA: Well, I guess readers of this series cannot use that excuse any more!

Are there several different types of low blood pressure?

MORITA: Yes. One type is known as secondary hypotension. This refers to low blood pressure which is caused by some illness.

TOYOFUKU: There is also orthostatic hypotension. This is when, for example, one stands up suddenly and the blood pressure drops, causing dizziness and a feeling of temporary weakness.

PRESIDENT IKEDA: What is the cause of orthostatic hypotension?

TOYOFUKU: The body is normally equipped with the ability to regulate blood pressure in the cases of sudden changes in posture. Some people suffer a disorder in this regulatory system which gives rise to low blood pressure.

Among the causes of secondary and orthostatic hypotension are illnesses of the nervous or endocrine systems, diabetes and the side effects of anti-hypertensive drugs.

PRESIDENT IKEDA: I see.

MORITA: Yet, another kind of low blood pressure is known as essential hypotension. As in the case of essential hypertension, we do not know what causes this. Most people with low blood pressure fall into this category.

TOYOFUKU: It is thought that genetic factors, environment, age and other physiological elements contribute to essential hypotension, but compared to high blood pressure, people suffering from this are at much lesser risk from stroke or heart attack. In fact, they tend to live longer than average.

Off to a Bright and Lively Start in the Morning

PRESIDENT IKEDA: There is no need to treat it, then?

TOYOFUKU: That is correct. With essential hypotension, unless one is experiencing some specific troubling symptom, there is no real need for treatment.

MORITA: Nevertheless, many people with essential hypotension do in fact suffer from various complaints, such as dizziness upon standing up, considerable difficulty in getting up in the morning, a feeling of lethargy, or a tendency to tire quickly.

PRESIDENT IKEDA: Perhaps some have gotten into the bad habit of staying up late at night and then oversleeping the next morning, without feeling the least bit restored or refreshed.

MORITA: That is very true. People with low blood pressure tend to fall very easily into the cycle of staying up late and sleeping late. They need to rethink their habits, especially those concerning eating and sleeping.

TOYOFUKU: It is especially important to eat breakfast, so that the brain begins functioning in peak condition from the morning.

President Ikeda: Extreme diets are dangerous for people with low blood pressure, aren't they?

Morita: Yes. People with low blood pressure need to get moderate exercise and work on increasing their strength. Cold wet-towel rubs or dry-towel rubs will also improve the blood circulation to the capillaries.

Toyofuku: People who have a really difficult time getting up in the morning should warm up while still in bed, starting by stretching and then doing a few very light exercises while lying down.

President Ikeda: We should strive to make the best use of our time during the day and then go to bed early. Then we can wake up the next morning full of energy and enthusiasm for another day's work. This is the secret to a long, healthy life. Our goal should be to create great value each day in the most reasonable and productive way.

Stress

Participants in this discussion on
' Humanism and the Art of Medicine:
A New Century of Health'
are SGI President Ikeda, Soka Gakkai
Doctors' Division Leaders Dr Shuhei Morita
and Dr Hiroyuki Toyofuku

PRESIDENT IKEDA: We live in a stressful society. Today, let us discuss the problem of stress.

MORITA: Yes. Around this time of the year in Japan, about a month or so after the new academic year and fiscal year have got under way at the beginning of April, we often hear of new students at a school or new employees at their workplace suffering from various psychosomatic ailments after the initial stress and tension of acclimatising to a new environment has worn off.

PRESIDENT IKEDA: Some call this particular adjustment disorder, "May sickness." But these days it seems variations of it are going around all year!

TOYOFUKU: Yes, in our modern technological society, more and more people are suffering from symptoms of stress to varying degrees. This is a sign of how chronic stress has become in our society.

The Meaning of Stress

PRESIDENT IKEDA: What exactly is stress?

TOYOFUKU: Stress is originally a term used in engineering and physics meaning the force exerted on an object.

MORITA: For example, when you press a rubber ball forcefully with your finger, you create an indentation. The condition in which the ball is under pressure by such exterior force is called stress.

PRESIDENT IKEDA: Who was the first to use the word *stress* as a medical term?

MORITA: Dr Hans Selye (1907-1982) of the University of Montreal in Canada, a pioneer in stress research, used it for the first time in an article written in 1935. He referred to the tension produced when a person receives a stimulus as 'stress' and the stimulus itself as the 'stressor'. Nowadays, we use the term *stress* to mean both the stimulus or origin of the tension and the reaction to it.

PRESIDENT IKEDA: What are some of the causes of stress?

TOYOFUKU: Well, there are physical or chemical causes of stress, such as heat, cold, injury or noise. And there are also physiological causes of stress, such as hunger, infection, or exhaustion.

MORITA: Those types of stress have been a part of human existence for a long time. People today are more likely to suffer from social or psychological stress, which includes things, such as human relations and pressures at work or school, financial anxiety, the illness or death of a family member or close friend, and accidents or natural disasters.

PRESIDENT IKEDA: Society today runs at a fast pace. It is fiercely competitive and regimented. Many feel constantly pressured and pursued by obligations and society's demands. At the same time, the human relationships that are so important to sustain people have grown weaker. There is a lack of a fundamental sense of security.

TOYOFUKU: That is why stress has become synonymous with modern society.

The Death of a Life Partner Causes the Greatest Stress

PRESIDENT IKEDA: Generally speaking, what causes people the greatest stress?

MORITA: Surveys show that, of all the events that occur in the normal course of our lives, the death of a spouse or life partner is most stressful. The next on the list is divorce or separation.

PRESIDENT IKEDA: Buddhism teaches that parting from loved ones is one of the eight inescapable sufferings of human existence.[1]

TOYOFUKU: Marriage is also one of the major causes of stress!

---

1. Eight sufferings: Eight kinds of universal suffering mentioned in the Nirvana and other sutras. They are the four sufferings of birth, old age, sickness and death, as well as the suffering of having to part from those whom one loves, the suffering of having to meet those whom one hates, the suffering of being unable to obtain what one desires, and the suffering arising from the five components which constitute one's body and mind.

PRESIDENT IKEDA: I am sure there are some who would rank it as the greatest cause! No matter how deeply two people may love each other, in the course of any long relationship, there are bound to be times when disagreements arise and quarrels ensue. At such times, you may feel that you cannot stand to even look at one another. That is another of the eight inescapable sufferings — having to interact with people we do not like!

We are all human, so it is only natural that human relationships should be the cause of our greatest joy and stress at the same time.

MORITA: Yes. And when that stress becomes severe, it affects our daily lives.

PRESIDENT IKEDA: Irritation is said to be a sign of an accumulation of stress. What are some of the symptoms of extreme stress?

TOYOFUKU: Tension, anxiety, apathy.

MORITA: If you go to see a doctor about such symptoms thinking they might be due to some illness, a general check-up will usually show that there is nothing wrong with you.

PRESIDENT IKEDA: Which only adds to the stress you feel! I am sure that happens, doesn't it?

Is there any way to actually measure stress?

MORITA: Yes. By measuring blood pressure and heart rate, checking ocular movement, taking a recording of brain waves and of muscular electrical activity, and combining those results with evaluations of psychological tests, we can assess the level of stress a person is experiencing.

Effects on the Autonomic Nervous System, Endocrine System and Immune System

PRESIDENT IKEDA: Stress must also affect us physically.

MORITA: Of course. Through the brain, it has a major effect on the functioning of the autonomic nervous system, the endocrine system and the immune system. For example, when a stressful state of anxiety or suffering persists, large amounts of adrenocortical hormones (steroid hormones secreted by the adrenal cortex) are produced. At the same time, the number of natural killer cells (NK cells), a subset of large granular lymphocytes, in circulation decreases, and the immune system is depressed.

TOYOFUKU: Since NK cells fight against cancer, stress creates a condition where one is more likely to be susceptible to the disease.

PRESIDENT IKEDA: So, stress can affect the progress of cancer. The workings of life are mysterious indeed. That is what we mean by 'mystic'. The body and the mind really are inextricably bound, aren't they?

MORITA: Yes, I believe so. Stress can also be deeply involved in stomach ulcers, duodenal ulcers, migraines, disorders of the autonomic nervous system, high blood pressure (hypertension), irregular heartbeat (arrhythmia) and asthma, as well as in Meniere's syndrome (a disorder characterised by recurrent bouts of dizziness), depression, anxiety neuroses and various phobias.

PRESIDENT IKEDA: What kind of stress-induced illnesses do you see frequently these days?

Causes for Stress

1. Physical or chemical causes of stress, such as heat, cold, injury or noise.
2. Physiological causes of stress, such as hunger, infection, or exhaustion.
3. Social or psychological stress, such as human relations and pressures at work or school, financial anxiety, illness or death of a family member or close friend, and accidents or natural disasters.

MORITA: Recently, irritable bowel syndrome seems to be common. It is a condition in which stress causes chronic diarrhoea, constipation, or stomach pains.

TOYOFUKU: Some afflicted with this condition often experience stomach pains when commuting to work or school, so they have memorised the location of every toilet in every station along the way.

Hope and a Sense of Mission Stimulate Life force

PRESIDENT IKEDA: The reaction to stress is different from person to person, isn't it?

TOYOFUKU: Yes. Individual factors, such as personality, behavioural patterns, lifestyle, values and whether or not there is support from friends and family, have a major impact on how stress affects a person.

PRESIDENT IKEDA: This is an extreme example, of course, but a survey was conducted of those who had experienced the Nazi concentration camps. Many people lost all hope upon their arrest. Some even committed suicide before they could be confined there. But among the survivors, we find many who say they were motivated to cling to life so that they could tell the world of this atrocity and ensure that it would never happen again.

Of course, I am not saying anything so facile as that all one needs to survive is hope. Many who were filled with precious hope died tragic deaths, nonetheless. What I am saying is that hope is the well-spring of life force. The death of hope is the death of the spirit. Nothing in this world is as strong as hope and a sense of mission.

By the way, what kind of people are most likely to be affected by stress?

MORITA: It is widely believed that those who demonstrate a certain set of character traits are particularly prone to stress. These people tend to be serious, responsible, conscientious, inflexible, perfectionist, without hobbies, concerned about how they are held in others' estimation, and unskilled in expressing their opinions and feelings.

TOYOFUKU: Of course, we are not saying it is a good idea to be frivolous and irresponsible, either.

Positive Thinking Stimulates the Immune System

MORITA: People who have a positive attitude are likely to take stress in stride more easily.

PRESIDENT IKEDA: You mean people who are positive thinkers?

Those in positions of leadership are subjected to a great deal of stress. But leaders must convert that stress into positive energy — into energy to tackle the next challenge.

TOYOFUKU: That is right. A survey was once conducted of some one thousand US business leaders. As a result of their high-ranking positions, all of them experienced a strong degree of isolation and stress. Yet, their mortality rate was more than thirty per cent below that of their contemporaries.

PRESIDENT IKEDA: I see. It is certainly true that those in positions of leadership are subjected to a great deal of stress. But leaders must convert that stress into positive energy — into energy to tackle the next challenge. People who are able to make the most of any circumstance they find themselves in are those who handle stress best. These are people who can create value. They aren't complainers.

MORITA: Each day is a fulfilling experience for such people. And, they are also highly resistant to illness.

TOYOFUKU: It is believed that positive thinking stimulates the production of endorphins in the brain and strengthens the immune system.

PRESIDENT IKEDA: Dr René Simard, the cancer specialist and rector of the University of Montreal, also told me that. In our dialogue [in December 1990], he remarked on the effects on endorphins, which he called "the body's natural morphine." Mr Toda also used to say that the body was a giant pharmaceutical plant. Buddhism expounds "the wonderful workings of one's mind." (*Gosho Zenshu*, pg 717) This mysterious nature of the mind is one of the key teachings of Buddhism.

Nichiren Daishonin writes, "Explaining the wonders of the mind is the prime objective of all sutras and treatises." (Gosho Zenshu, *pg 564*)

Life is inherently endowed with the marvellous capacity to convert even the negative into something positive. At the most basic level, one's life is created by one's own inner resolve, one's mind. This is even more true of a person with faith.

The same is true of stress. The question is whether we use stress as the wind beneath our wings to soar high into the sky or whether we allow ourselves to be blown away by it. We each have the capacity to decide that by our own mind or inner resolve.

TOYOFUKU: In that sense, stress is an indispensable element in living a better life.

PRESIDENT IKEDA: Precisely. An aeroplane cannot fly without the resistance of the air that lifts it. By the same token, when we lack any resistance, when we have no problems to challenge us, we can lose our focus and sense of direction. It all depends on whether we can put the wind to good use.

Of course, we need to make efforts to improve our environment. But even so, there will always be some degree of stress as long as we are alive. The important thing is to learn how to handle stress.

MORITA: Yes, I think that is the essential point. Let us discuss ways of coping with stress in our next discussion.

PRESIDENT IKEDA: Today, we are going to discuss handling stress. I hope waiting a week for this instalment did not cause any of our readers stress!

MORITA: I certainly hope not, too. When we talk about managing stress, it is important to remember that there are many, many different options. At the same time, there is no magic cure-all for stress.

TOYOFUKU: I think the best method for managing stress is to have a positive and forward-looking attitude.

PRESIDENT IKEDA: The positive thinking that we talked about last time.

MORITA: Yes. Many of those most susceptible to stress tend to care too much about what others think. They also tend to have rigid ideas about themselves, a rigid conception of how they should be and what they should think.

TOYOFUKU: Such people tend, as a result of those traits, to gradually lose their ability to express their true feelings.

Do not Compare Yourself with Others

PRESIDENT IKEDA: I see. You are saying that we should be true to ourselves. If we are always comparing ourselves to others or caring too much about what others think, we are cramping and limiting ourselves.

Each of us is the star of our own life story, the hero and protagonist. The best way to live is to make our own decisions and follow our own convictions. We should each feel free to be ourselves. Worrying too much about what others think will never make one happy, anyway.

Life is inherently endowed with the marvellous capacity to convert even the negative into something positive. At the most basic level, one's life is created by one's own inner resolve, one's mind. This is even more true of a person with faith.

Is it not true that people who live a long time tend to be optimists?

MORITA: Yes. A survey was once carried out in Okinawa, the Japanese prefecture with the highest percentage of residents one hundred years old or older. Most of those surveyed were described as 'cheerful', 'lively', 'optimistic', 'straightforward', and 'having a large circle of friends'.

PRESIDENT IKEDA: One's state of mind is also an important factor in how long one lives, then.

Humour and laughter are also an important means of relieving stress, aren't they?

MORITA: Yes, they are. We have the expression 'to laugh until one's sides ache' and, in fact, when we laugh we breathe very deeply from our diaphragm, taking in a lot of oxygen, which has the effect of improving the blood flow. It keeps irritation at bay.

TOYOFUKU: When we laugh, the brain releases hormones that relieve pain and stimulate our immune system.

PRESIDENT IKEDA: The German philosopher, Immanuel Kant (1724-1804), asserted that laughter is far more beneficial for the body than a doctor's medicine.

Kant wrote: "[Whatever provokes it,] laughter is always a shaking of the muscles involved in digestion, which promotes it far better than the physician's wisdom would do."[2]

MORITA: Doesn't the English word humour in fact come from a Latin term meaning 'bodily fluid'?

PRESIDENT IKEDA: Yes, it does. Hippocrates, the ancient Greek physician known as the father of Western medicine, believed that the body contained four fluids.[3] Good health was the state in which these four 'humours' were in proper balance.

TOYOFUKU: Some people say that they relieve stress by shopping, or making long phone calls.

PRESIDENT IKEDA: Those may well be ways to relieve stress, but they certainly aren't very economical.

MORITA: That is certainly true. Nevertheless, it is important to have friends with whom one can talk freely and consult about anything.

TOYOFUKU: Yes, worrying about something all by yourself is never fruitful. You are likely to get stuck in a vicious cycle of pessimism.

PRESIDENT IKEDA: Yes. Those who have someone with whom they can talk

---

2. Immanuel Kant, Anthropology from a Pragmatic Point of View, trans Mary J. Gregor (The Hague: Martinus Nijhoff, 1074), pg 129.
3. Four 'humours': Blood, phlegm, choler and black bile.

things over are truly fortunate. It is wonderful that we have so many friends we can talk to in the SGI. In particular, elderly people who have friends they can talk to tend to be more physically and emotionally stable and healthy.

TOYOFUKU: Specialists in the field of psychosomatic medicine refer to the friends a person can rely on and who provide an emotional safety net as 'supporters'. Such friendship and support are very important elements in coping with stress.

Being a Good Listener

PRESIDENT IKEDA: What is the best way one can offer support to others?

MORITA: The most important thing is to be a good listener.

TOYOFUKU: I am reminded of the experience of a member of the Shirakaba-kai, the Soka Gakkai Women's Division nurses' group. She was assigned to care for an eighty-seven-year-old woman. When she first met her patient, the old woman sat listlessly in a wheelchair with a bored expression, her lips tightly pressed together and her eyebrows knitted together in a permanent frown.

When this nurse first saw her, she was filled with the desire to make her charge smile, to bring a warm expression to her face. From that time, whenever they met she would take the elderly woman's hand and speak to her. Then one day, in the hospital coffee shop, the patient began to share all that she had suffered in her life. The nurse held her hand as always and just listened — patiently following the story and nodding in acknowledgement.

When the patient had finished speaking, the nurse picked her up and carried her back to her room. En route, the woman whispered to her new friend, "No one has ever listened to me like that before." And from that day on, a smile shone brightly on the elderly woman's face.

PRESIDENT IKEDA: What a beautiful story!

Yes, listening is so important. Those who can really listen to others have a warm capacity to reach out and embrace other people. That capacity to give thought to others is in itself a sign of good health, the energy from which sound health derives. Just having someone listen to you can be very therapeutic, making you feel much better.

Showing Understanding and Consideration

TOYOFUKU: Yes. When someone is exhausted from stress, vigorous encouragement can make things worse.

PRESIDENT IKEDA: It is very important to listen quietly and patiently to others and to show them you understand.

TOYOFUKU: The understanding and concern of those around us, particularly our families, are indispensable. For instance, if spouses or partners rarely have time to see one another, because one or both are always late coming home from work or activities, they should endeavour to create regular opportunities for communication, even if it means sharing a pot of tea together at midnight.

PRESIDENT IKEDA: In one sense, it is important for couples to be compassionate and generous towards each other. Of course, an entirely different approach is necessary if one party constantly makes 'stress relief' an excuse for going out drinking every night and ignoring personal commitments!

MORITA: Yes. A person like that does not deserve a lot of sympathy.

TOYOFUKU: Drinking and eating out of frustration, far from being a kind of stress relief, actually harm one's health.

PRESIDENT IKEDA: Sleep is good medicine for stress, isn't it?

MORITA: Yes, rest is very important. When one feels that an uncomfortable level of stress has built up, one must take sufficient time to relax and recuperate.

TOYOFUKU: Recuperation can take the form of sleep, nutritious food, a warm bath, or light exercise. If one is experiencing only a slight degree of stress, rest and nutritious food will be sufficient for recovery.

PRESIDENT IKEDA: Yes, but it can be very difficult to find time to recuperate when one has a lot of work to do.

MORITA: That is true. The secret is to use your time wisely and find ways to give yourself a refreshing change of pace. We should all make sure we have time to relax every day, even if it is only ten or fifteen minutes. You can relax however you like — listening to music, enjoying a hobby, or whatever else suits you.

TOYOFUKU: You can divide your time into 'work time' and 'relaxation time', bringing some variety to your life.

PRESIDENT IKEDA: Sometimes one gets so tired that it is impossible to sleep, no matter how hard one tries.

MORITA: After you have passed a certain stress threshold, you reach a state in which nothing you do seem to help, and attempts to relieve stress only make you more tired. Nothing makes you feel any better.

TOYOFUKU: That is a danger signal. You have passed tiredness and entered the state of exhaustion.

PRESIDENT IKEDA: Buddhism also teaches that exhaustion is one of the conditions conducive to illness.[4]

WAYS TO OVERCOME STRESS

1. **Have a positive and forward-looking attitude.**
2. **Laugh.**
3. **Have friends with whom one can talk freely and consult about anything.**
4. **Live by a personal philosophy and have a fulfilling goal in life.**
5. **Divide your time into 'work time' and 'relaxation time', bringing some variety to our lives.**

In recent years, there has been much concern in Japan about death caused by overwork. Does stress play any part in such desire?

MORITA: The direct cause of death in such cases is usually heart attack or stroke. In many cases, the victim has a chronic illness, such as diabetes or high blood pressure, which is brought to a crisis point by extreme physical or emotional stress.

---

4. From the *Butsui* Sutra (Sutra of Buddhist Medicine).

Toyofuku: If you have persistent sleeplessness or depression, or if you experience such stress-related symptoms as migraines or diarrhoea, it is advisable to see a doctor who specialises in treating psychosomatic disorders.

President Ikeda: More and more people are complaining of such physical and emotional upsets brought on by trying to 'keep up' in a competitive society and stay apace with the continuous changes in technology. Things have obviously reached the point where we can no longer leave it entirely up to the individual to combat the problem of stress and stress-induced illnesses. Employers and society as a whole must start work in finding some way to solve this problem.

Morita: That is very true. And, recently more companies are employing specialists in psychiatry and psychosomatic medicine, and bringing counsellors into the workplace, out of their concern for the emotional and physical health of their workers.

President Ikeda: I guest there are also some people who get sick, without even noticing that they are stressed.

Morita: Yes. There are people who do not notice stress, even when it has begun to take its emotional and physical toll on them.

Being Careful Not to Push Oneself beyond Reason

Toyofuku: We see this most often in people who are always trying too hard or who are very sensitive to others' needs and wants. Such types overrespond to their environment.

President Ikeda: They push themselves too hard, running themselves into the ground.

There is a difference between earnest effort and overdoing things. If you drive yourself too hard, you won't be able to keep it up for very long. Earnest effort, on the other hand, is characterised by steady progress that accords with reason.

If we are motivated and earnestly involved in some endeavour, we will experience an energy that stress can not take away. On the other hand, if we drop our guard and just sit there day dreaming, we allow a crack to open in our mental armour whereby stress can then readily invade our life.

Toyofuku: I think we need to be able to view our own physical and emotional state objectively.

Morita: Earlier, we said that recuperation is important. That does not mean, however, that you will be refreshed and revitalised just by lazing about the house doing nothing.

Toyofuku: In fact, getting involved in some project or activity is what really refreshes one mentally and physically.

President Ikeda: If we are motivated and earnestly involved in some endeavour, we will experience an energy that stress can not take away. On the other hand, if we drop our guard and just sit there day dreaming, we allow a crack to open in our mental armour whereby stress can then readily invade our life.

Toyofuku: Viruses and other pathogens also exploit such vulnerable moments.

President Ikeda: We must not be passive. That leaves us open to attack.
A life on the offensive, on the other hand, means seeking a challenge that inspires us, advancing towards our dream. That determination and passion

becomes the strength that enables us to cope with stress. In that sense, how successfully we deal with stress depends on whether we have a fulfilling goal in life. It is a matter of the personal philosophy we live by.

MORITA: That is true. Another way of refreshing oneself is to place oneself in new human relationships, interacting with people who have different experiences and backgrounds.

PRESIDENT IKEDA: When you increase the size of your world, you can awaken a 'new you' and increase your enjoyment of life tremendously.

> **Buddhism teaches that earthly desires are enlightenment. Life is never completely free from sufferings. Problems, rather, are the motivation for effort and progress. When we strengthen our life force through the Mystic Law, all earthly desires and suffering are instantly transformed into enlightenment. Problems are transformed into wisdom, into happiness. The same is true of stress. Stress forces us to pay attention to our health. Stress, too, serves as an impetus for growth, for developing our life-condition.**

MORITA: In that respect, SGI activities can be a great way to relieve stress, too!

PRESIDENT IKEDA: In Buddhism, nothing is in vain. Of course, having faith does not mean we will never experience stress. In some respects, working for the sake of others is always accompanied by great expenditure of energy, and it may result in deep fatigue. But that is what makes our endeavours so noble. And, that is why our lives are strengthened and grow even healthier. Buddhism teaches that earthly desires are enlightenment. Life is never completely free from sufferings. Problems, rather, are the motivation for effort and progress. When we strengthen our life force through the Mystic Law, all earthly desires and suffering are instantly transformed into enlightenment. Problems are transformed into wisdom, into happiness.

The same is true of stress. Stress forces us to pay attention to our health. Stress, too, serves as an impetus for growth, for developing our life-condition.

One of the names of the Buddha is 'One Who Can Forbear'. That strength, that power to survive, is the life state of the Buddha. I hope all our members will learn to navigate our stress-riddled society smoothly, with positive thinking and good cheer.

Lower Back Pain

Participants in this discussion on
' Humanism and the Art of Medicine:
A New Century of Health'
are SGI President Ikeda, Soka Gakkai
Doctors' Division Leaders Dr Shuhei Morita
and Dr Hiroyuki Toyofuku

PRESIDENT IKEDA: What is the most crucial part of our bodies? Of course, there are many possible answers to this question, but the back is certainly very important.

The Chinese character for the lower back or hip area (read in Japanese as *koshi* or *yō*) combines the component for 'flesh', on the left, with the character for *kaname*, meaning 'crux', on the right. The meaning of the character is, very appropriately, the crux or the most essential part of the body. In fact, the character *kaname* itself is a pictograph of the hipbone.

Many people seem to suffer from lower back pain.

MORITA: Yes, indeed. The most commonly performed operations by orthopaedic surgeons are those for back pain in the lumbar region.

TOYOFUKU: I myself have suffered from back problems. It all started when I had to sleep in a very soft bed once when I was travelling.

PRESIDENT IKEDA: That was a valuable experience. As they say, "You will never be a good doctor if you have not been sick yourself."

TOYOFUKU: And, how true that is!

The Lower Back Supports Sixty Per Cent of the Body's Weight

PRESIDENT IKEDA: Why is it that so many people suffer from lower back problems?

MORITA: To put it simply, the lower back is the weak point of our species. Only human beings walk upright. That has freed us to use our hands for other things, but it also means that our lower back carries the weight of our entire upper body.

PRESIDENT IKEDA: I see. Back problems are, in a way, the fate of our species.

TOYOFUKU: Yes. The lower part or lumbar region of the spine supports sixty per cent of our body weight. Between each of the vertebrae in the spinal column there is an intervertebral disc, which functions like a cushion.

PRESIDENT IKEDA: The intervertebral discs soften heavy loads and absorb shocks and stress, right?

TOYOFUKU: Yes. In addition, the lower spine is supported by ligaments, which connect the bones to each other, as well as by the stomach muscles and the back muscles.

MORITA: When the back and stomach muscles are strong, the back is well supported. When those muscles are weak, a relatively small shock can put stress on the lower vertebrae, which we experience as pain.

In fact, this kind of lower back pain, which is not caused by any disease, is by far the most common back problem.

PRESIDENT IKEDA: I guess that includes 'throwing one's back out'?

MORITA: Yes. 'To throw one's back out' is a way of describing sudden and urgent back pain that can be caused by any number of things.

PRESIDENT IKEDA: In German, they call throwing one's back out 'a witch's stab'. Suddenly a sharp, cruel pain shoots through one — an apt description, don't you think?

TOYOFUKU: I cringe just to think of it!

Those Who Work in the Same Position for a Long Time Suffer the Most

PRESIDENT IKEDA: What kinds of people are most likely to experience back pain?

MORITA: People who are confined to a desk all day, or those who drive long distances at a stretch — in other words, people who are forced in their work to remain in a single position for a long period of time. Overweight people also have back problems quite often.

PRESIDENT IKEDA: Who are more likely to have back problems, women or men?

TOYOFUKU: Women. Compared to men, the strength of their back and stomach muscles is lower. Women are also likely to experience back pain at meno-

People are most likely to experience back pain — who are confined to a desk all day, or those who drive long distances at a stretch — in other words, people who are forced in their work to remain in a single position for a long period of time.

pause, because of hormone imbalances, and before and after childbirth.

PRESIDENT IKEDA: Can back pain also be caused by some spinal disorder?

MORITA: Yes, the most frequent cause of this kind is rupture or slipped discs. This is especially common among people in their twenties and thirties.

TOYOFUKU: 'Hernia' means 'protrusion'. The intervertebral discs of the spinal column are filled with a jelly-like matter, covered by a resilient cartilage. From our early twenties, that cartilage gradually begins to lose some of its resiliency. When that happens, the jelly inside can protrude and place pressure on a spinal nerve.

Maintaining Physical Fitness

PRESIDENT IKEDA: Lack of exercise is the cause, then?

MORITA: Yes. With the spread of the automobile and other labour-saving devices, many of us do not walk or get as much physical exercise as we once did.

PRESIDENT IKEDA: It is important to exercise and strengthen both your body and mind in your twenties and thirties. That training will build a base for the rest of your life; it will serve as a magnificent foundation on which to further build and develop yourself. The same is true of health.

Of course, there is considerable difference from one person to another, but in general, from your forties on, maintaining and preserving your physical strength becomes more important than increasing it. The wise path is to train at the time in your life when training will be most effective, and to preserve your health and fitness when preservation is most beneficial.

TOYOFUKU: That is certainly true. There are a few other disorders that can cause back pain — for example, spondylosis and osteoporosis.[1]

PRESIDENT IKEDA: I have heard that certain diseases of the internal organs can also cause back pain?

It is important to exercise and strengthen both your body and mind in your twenties and thirties. That training will build a base for the rest of your life; it will serve as a magnificent foundation on which to further build and develop yourself. The same is true of health.

TOYOFUKU: Yes. Kidney stones, gallstones, stomach ulcers and pancreatic inflammation can all cause lower back pain.

PRESIDENT IKEDA: What should one do for a sore back?

MORITA: The most important thing is to rest, and if the pain is really intense, to rest until the pain is substantially reduced.

TOYOFUKU: If the pain remains intense, one should consult a doctor, who will most probably prescribe some medicine to relieve the pain and reduce inflammation.

PRESIDENT IKEDA: Is it better to apply heat or cold compresses to a sore back?

---

1. Spondylosis is an inflammation of the spine and osteoporosis is a disease characterised by a marked decrease in bone mass.

Morita: When the pain is very severe, it is usually better to apply cold compresses to bring down the inflammation. Once the pain has lessened somewhat, it is probably better to keep the back warm. A warm — not hot — bath can be soothing.

President Ikeda: I think that many people just try to put up with the pain. But in this case, patient endurance is not a virtue, is it?

Toyofuku: No, it is not. Persistent pain can have an adverse effect on the body.

Morita: When we experience pain, the nerves send the stimulus to the brain, which in turn causes spasms of the muscles and constriction of the blood vessels at the site of the pain. This results in poor circulation, and the muscles clench and become stiffer, which again stimulates the nerves, causing additional pain.

President Ikeda: I see. One effect becomes the cause of another effect, creating a vicious circle of pain.

Morita: Ignoring back pain only backfires!

President Ikeda: And then, tasks that you want to really 'put your back into' will end up as 'back-breaking' jobs!

Avoid Overexerting Your Back

President Ikeda: How can lower back pain be avoided?

Toyofuku: The most important step one can take is not to overexert the back. We can start by examining the way we stand up, the way we sit, and the way we sleep.

Morita: The best way to stand up is to pull in your chin, straighten your back, and pull in your stomach. A hunched posture places considerable stress on the lower back. One should also avoid standing with the stomach and hips pushed out in front. Aside from stressing your back, it is not a very attractive posture, either.

Lie down upward, letting the waist down on the floor, bend the legs and count three times. Later, straighten the legs. (Repeat this three times.)

Lie down upward, slowly pull up the knees towards the chest. Use the hands to hold down the knees, count three times. (Repeat this three times.)

Lie down upward, bend the knees with both feet placed firmly on the floor. Slowly count until five. Later, raise the shoulders up slowly, about 25cm away from the floor. Maintain this position for five seconds before returning to the initial position. (Repeat this three times.)

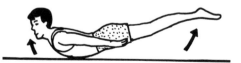

Lie downward. With hands firmly by the side of the body, give yourself a tight pull upwardly. Count five times. (Repeat this five times.)

PRESIDENT IKEDA: I'll bet that arrogant and conceited people who are always swaggering about are more likely to have back problems, then.

Good Posture is the Secret to Youth and Health

PRESIDENT IKEDA: Good posture gives an impression of energy and alertness. When one stands up straight and tall not only does one look better, but it undoubtedly also improves the circulation and stimulates the nerves as well, thus promoting good health.

Whatever one's age, good posture is the secret to looking good. By making a little effort in this department, we can remain youthful mentally and physically.

MORITA: That is certainly true. As for the best postures for sleep, curled up on one's side or lying on one's back with a small pillow under the knees is said to be most healthful.

TOYOFUKU: And, please avoid very soft mattresses that your body sinks into!

PRESIDENT IKEDA: Yes, you have had a personal experience with that, haven't you?

MORITA: When sitting, you should sit all the way back in the chair, not on its edge. The best chair is a little lower, so that when seated your knees are a bit higher than your thighs.

TOYOFUKU: Sitting properly is important, but the biggest problem is when you have to sit in the same position for a long time.

PRESIDENT IKEDA: These days some people spend the entire day sitting in front of a word processor or computer.

MORITA: It is important to take breaks regularly, no matter how brief. One should get up from one's desk at least once an hour, just to take a trip to the rest room or walk to the window and look out. This will refresh one both mentally and physically.

Sitting on the Floor

TOYOFUKU: When sitting on the floor, sitting on your legs tucked under you puts less stress on your back than sitting cross-legged.

PRESIDENT IKEDA: That seems reasonable. The Great Teacher T'ien-t'ai spoke of "regulating the five activities," as part of Buddhist practice.[2] The five activities are eating, sleeping, posture, breathing and thinking. When all of those activities are properly regulated, our minds and bodies are stable. These are part of the preparation essential for establishing communication between our own life and the totality of being, the universe.

TOYOFUKU: If one sits up straight with the legs tucked underneath, the blood can circulate smoothly.

MORITA: Though it hurts to sit that way, if you are overweight!

PRESIDENT IKEDA: All the more reason to go on a diet!
Are there any other simple tricks to avoiding back pain?

TOYOFUKU: When lifting anything, no matter how light it is, lift from the legs. In other words, instead of just bending over stiff-legged, squat down and then push up with your legs. When lifting heavy things, keep them as close to your body as you can and bend your knees slightly. That will protect your back.

PRESIDENT IKEDA: It is also good to be consciously aware of lifting. Before you start, say to yourself, "All right, I'm going to lift something heavy now."

MORITA: Yes. In any action, if you simply react without thinking, there is no time for your brain to control the movement. You begin to lift without giving the muscles in your lower back time to prepare to do so. That often leads to throwing your back out.

---

2. In the *Maka Shikan* (Great Concentration and Insight), T'ien-t'ai lists 'regulating the five activities' among his twenty-five preparatory exercises, which he posited as essential to develop one's capability to realise the true nature of life.

Walking is good for strengthening the back. When you walk with long strides and swing your arms, you improve your circulation and feel more energetic.

TOYOFUKU: Cold temperatures or catching chills can also be a major culprit in back pain. It is a good idea to keep your lower back area warm.

MORITA: It is also important to strengthen the lower back muscles. So in that respect, moderate exercise is highly recommended.

PRESIDENT IKEDA: What kind of exercise is good for strengthening the back?

TOYOFUKU: Walking is the easiest for most people to do. When you walk with long strides and swing your arms, you improve your circulation and feel more energetic.

There are also various exercises for easing back pain — which, incidentally, can help one lose weight, too.

MORITA: It takes at least three months to see the effects of exercises for strengthening the back and the stomach muscles, so it is probably best to find a set of exercises that you can enjoy and make an ongoing part of your daily routine.

Those who are suffering from back pain, however, should wait until the pain subsides and then check with their doctor before beginning any programme of exercise.

The Back Supports the 'Treasure Tower'

President Ikeda: At the start of this instalment, I remarked that the back is the crux of the body. Buddhism teaches that the body of each of us is the entity of the Buddha, that it is the Treasure Tower. In that sense, the back is the crucial element that supports the Treasure Tower.

In the Ongi Kuden (Record of the Orally Transmitted Teachings), Nichiren Daishonin says: "[With regard to the five characters of Myoho-renge-kyo,] myo is the head, ho is the neck, ren is the chest, ge is the belly, and kyo is the legs. Our five-foot body is the five characters of Myoho-renge-kyo." (Gosho Zenshu, pg 716) He further states: "The Treasure Tower is also nothing other than the five characters of Myoho-renge-kyo. According to the Lotus Sutra, the Treasure Tower represents all living beings. Thus, all living beings are Nam-myoho-renge-kyo itself in its entirety." (Gosho Zenshu, pg 797)

When we dedicate our life, body and mind to the True Law, our entire being will shine as a Treasure Tower of the Mystic Law, and we will enjoy both mental and physical health. Of this, there is not the slightest doubt.

I hope all our members will make a commitment to being healthier, and work to achieve that end so that they can pursue their endeavours with joy, and with light and eager steps.

Teeth

Participants in this discussion on
' Humanism and the Art of Medicine:
A New Century of Health'
are SGI President Ikeda, Soka Gakkai
Doctors' Division Leaders Dr Shuhei Morita,
Dr Hiroyuki Toyofuku and special guest,
dental hygienist, Esumi Sato

MORITA: June 4 marks the beginning of Dental Hygiene Week in Japan. To coincide with that, we have invited dental hygienist, Esumi Sato, to join us for our discussion, which will focus on dental health.

SATO: It is my pleasure to be here today.

PRESIDENT IKEDA: Please make yourselves comfortable and join right in. I hope you will give us some good advice, straight from the hygienist's mouth, so to speak.

It seems there are many people who don't really like going to the dentist.

TOYOFUKU: That is true. In fact, some people suddenly get a headache just thinking about the high whine of the dentist's drill!

Strong Teeth are One of the Thirty-two Features of a Buddha

PRESIDENT IKEDA: How many teeth do human beings have?

SATO: Adults have thirty-two teeth, if we include the four wisdom teeth.

MORITA: It is said that Sakyamuni had forty teeth.

PRESIDENT IKEDA: We do not know whether he really did or not. But teeth are mentioned among the list of the thirty-two features (remarkable physical characteristics) of a Buddha, which includes 'forty teeth', 'even teeth' and 'four white fangs'.

It seems that even from ancient times, people have admired good teeth. Nichiren Daishonin also mentions 'white teeth' as a feature of beauty (cf *Gosho Zenshu*, pg 395).

SATO: Yes. By far the majority of people today admire white teeth. But generally speaking, very white teeth tend to be a bit weak. Teeth that are slightly yellow are actually more natural in colour and stronger, too.

PRESIDENT IKEDA: Is that so?

Brushing is the Only Way to Prevent Cavities

PRESIDENT IKEDA: Has the cause of tooth decay been identified?

SATO: Yes, for the most part. A bacteria called *Streptococcus mutans* is now thought to be a main cause of tooth decay. This bacteria lives on sugar, from which it makes a sticky, paste-like material that does not dissolve in water. Living in this paste, the bacteria reproduces on the surface of the teeth, gradually creating a layer. This is plaque.

TOYOFUKU: It is the white paste that one can scrape off the surface of a tooth with a toothpick, for example.

SATO: Yes. Many different types of bacteria make their homes in this plaque. They decompose the food left between the teeth, creating acid. The acid eats away at the outer enamel layer of the tooth, which is how a cavity begins.

PRESIDENT IKEDA: I see. Is there any medicine to prevent cavities?

SATO: Unfortunately, no. Only proper brushing can prevent cavities. Brushing one's teeth is the best and only way to remove plaque and create an environment in which decay-producing bacteria cannot live.

PRESIDENT IKEDA: That cannot be overemphasised.

MORITA: I agree. And as someone with bad teeth, I have to say that this is the medical truth.

PRESIDENT IKEDA: Shakespeare said, "For there was never yet philosopher / That could endure the toothache patiently."[1] I guess the same goes for doctors!
    Is a propensity to cavities hereditary?

SATO: The formation of cavities is not due to heredity. People frequently say that they have bad teeth because their parents did, but whether you have cavities depends entirely upon your care of your teeth.

---

1. William Shakespeare, *Much Ado About Nothing*, volume I, 35 (1598).

When I was a child, I had cavities in all of my primary teeth, which caused serious irregularities in the alignment of my permanent teeth when they finally came. But I made sure to brush my teeth regularly and with careful thoroughness from that time on, so my permanent teeth have been very healthy.

Steering Clear of Tooth Decay Culprits

PRESIDENT IKEDA: Advice based on experience can be more persuasive than a thousand medical texts.

What kinds of food lead to cavities?

SATO: Cakes and cookies, sweet drinks and candy.

MORITA: Greasy snack foods, such as potato chips also create a sticky environment in the mouth, don't they?

SATO: Yes. People who are always snacking on sweets or highly refined carbohydrate foods are creating an acid environment in their mouths that is perfect for the development of the bacteria that cause tooth decay. Snacking on junk food is really a major problem in this regard.

PRESIDENT IKEDA: What, on the other hand, are relatively good foods for the teeth?

SATO: Small fish with very fragile, edible bones are thought to be good: They provide calcium and phosphorus, from which teeth are made, as well as fluoride, which also strengthens the teeth.

TOYOFUKU: That is why green tea, which contains fluoride, is also said to be good for the teeth.

SATO: Yes. Actually, the permanent teeth begin to form while the infant is still in the mother's womb, so it is also important for pregnant women to eat a nutritionally balanced diet.

PRESIDENT IKEDA: Why do people today seem to have more cavities than their ancestors?

MORITA: The most important factor would seem to be the change in our diet. The foods we eat have, through changes in cooking methods and advances in food processing technology, become substantially softer and more refined. As a result, we do not chew as much as we once did. This is thought to be one reason why our jaws have become smaller and our teeth weaker.

SATO: That is true. And, as our jaws have gone smaller it has adversely affected the arrangement of our teeth. The wisdom teeth of some seventy-five per cent of all Japanese do not come in correctly — the reason being that there is no longer any room to accommodate them.

We Chew Far Less than Our Ancestors

TOYOFUKU: According to research, Japanese living in the Yayoi period (a pre-historic period in Japan dating from about 300 BC to 300 AD) chewed each meal 3,990 times.

MORITA: That must have been some feat of research!

TOYOFUKU: Yes, indeed. But Japanese today chew each meal an average of only 620 times — less than one-sixth the times of their Yayoi forebears.

THE EFFECTS OF CHEWING

1. **Prevent cavities.**
2. **Enzymes in saliva assist in one's digestion.**
3. **Saliva also contains enzymes that eliminate toxin that promote the growth of cancer.**
4. **Prevent against overeating and becoming overweight.**
5. **Help slow down the process of senility and the deterioration of the brain.**

PRESIDENT IKEDA: Only one-sixth? That is astonishing. It would seem that in the past our teeth and jaws were challenged, and as a result strengthened, by being called upon to deal with tougher, more chewable foods.

The same principle applies to people. In a comfortable, sheltered situation, one loses the ability to rise to a challenge. But when we face a tough situation, a problem we can 'sink our teeth into', we can grow and even tap hidden strength.

'Magical Elixir of the Fountain of Youth'

PRESIDENT IKEDA: What effects does chewing have?

SATO: First, it develops the jaw. When the jaw is weak, the teeth come in badly and it becomes harder to care for them. It also makes it easier for plaque to accumulate.

MORITA: The more one chews, the more saliva is secreted. This is important because the enzymes in saliva assist in one's digestion.

SATO: Saliva also functions to wash away the crumbs of food stuck between the teeth. It neutralises acid and slows the growth of bacteria, helping to prevent cavities and other dental problems.

TOYOFUKU: Saliva also contains enzymes that eliminate toxin that promote the growth of cancers, and it contains hormones that help keep us young.

PRESIDENT IKEDA: Though it may be a bit of an over-statement, we might call saliva a sort of magical elixir of the fountain of youth. Another positive benefit of chewing is that it makes one feel full before the stomach is actually completely full.

MORITA: Yes, so it can help prevent against overeating and becoming over-weight. Chewing also stimulates the brain. It is said, for instance, that if you chew bubble gum while driving — especially on a long journey — it helps you stay awake. The chewing gum is not what does the trick; it is the action of chewing, which improves circulation to the head and activates the brain. Chewing can also, then, help slow down the process of senility and the deterioration of the brain.

PRESIDENT IKEDA: Chewing is an important element in health and for living a long life. We might even call it a symbol of the will to live, the strength to survive.

TOYOFUKU: Exactly. Being able to chew is really essential if we are going to enjoy eating. When eating is no longer a pleasure — because of the loss of a tooth or other dental problems, for instance — some people may even lose the will to go on living altogether.

The Loss of One Molar Reduces Chewing Power by Forty Per Cent

MORITA: The Japanese Ministry of Health and Welfare has introduced a new campaign called the '80-20 Movement'. The name stands for the goal of retaining at least twenty of one's teeth to the age of eighty. It is held that if one has twenty teeth, one can eat practically any kind of food with relative ease.

PRESIDENT IKEDA: How many teeth on average does an eighty-year-old Japanese person have?

SATO: Four or five. People of the same age in some areas of America have as many as ten.

PRESIDENT IKEDA: That seems to reflect the low awareness we Japanese tend to have about the importance of taking care of our teeth. Though I am sure social customs and the costs of dental treatment also play a part in the difference.

SATO: Some people in Japan are not too reluctant to have a tooth pulled out. They think, "Oh, it's just one tooth." But in fact, the loss of one molar reduces one's overall chewing efficiency by forty per cent. Some no doubt console themselves by saying they can always get false teeth. But no matter how well-made false teeth are, they are no match for our natural teeth.

MORITA: There are also times when a filling does not match one's bite very well. That can be very irritating.

SATO: The periodontal membrane that lies at the root of a tooth softens the pressure exerted on the jawbone in chewing. This membrane is extremely sensitive — it can sense a difference as narrow as a single hair. Teeth are much more sophisticated than we are inclined to believe.

PRESIDENT IKEDA: There is a saying that "There are two things you don't appreciate until you lose them: your teeth and happiness." It is really true, isn't it? Losing all your teeth can have a traumatic emotional impact as well. When your teeth are nicely aligned and your smile is attractive, it is easy to find talking with others enjoyable no matter how old you are. In Japan, many people who lose their teeth feel somewhat reluctant to meet and talk with others.

SATO: Actually, it literally does become harder to speak when you have no teeth. It also has an effect on your facial expressions. Some people become embarrassed to open their mouth and to socialise with others.

TOYOFUKU: But one common characteristics of those who enjoy long lives is maintaining an active social life and not withdrawing into one's own shell.

PRESIDENT IKEDA: In China, whether you still have your own teeth is seen as precondition for good health and longevity.

There is a Chinese expression which literally translates as "to lose one's teeth," — an expression found in such classics as the *Analects* of Confucius — which means to come to the end of one's life. In other words, 'teeth' stand for life. In fact, the Chinese character for years or age (Jpn *rei*) comes from the character for teeth. In ancient times, people's age and length of life were measured by their teeth. There is another word also meaning age (Jpn *nenshi*), which is written with the characters 'years' and 'teeth'.

Also, in China and Japan in the past, there was a custom called 'hardening the teeth', which consisted of eating something hard for the first time in the New Year as a sort of prayer or charm for a long life. It is described in such works of the Japanese literature as *The Tale of Genji*, written in the early 11th century, and *The Tosa Diary*, written in 935.

Our teeth are a precious mainstay of life. We have to take care of them.

MORITA: How should each of us best care for our teeth? In our next instalment, let us discuss the best way to brush our teeth as well as various dental diseases.

TOYOFUKU: I thought I understood how important dental health is, but I must admit I have never noticed that the Chinese character for age (Jpn *rei* or *yowai*) derives from the character for teeth.

MORITA: Our teeth are indeed our life, so it seems.

PRESIDENT IKEDA: This way of viewing teeth is not restricted to the East. Hippocrates, the father of Western medicine, is supposed to have said that the long-lived have many teeth; in other words, a healthy person has strong teeth that last into old age.

By the way, cavities are not the only diseases affecting the teeth, are they?

SATO: No. The teeth themselves are important, but so are the gums and other parts of the structure that supports the teeth. Dental health means that both the teeth and their supporting structure are healthy.

PRESIDENT IKEDA: I see. I wonder if it is not like the relationship between a building and the foundation that supports it. If the foundation is crumbling, it really does not matter how fine the building may be.

Bleeding Gums are a Sign of Trouble

SATO: Yes. Inflammations of the structure that supports the teeth — the foundation, if you will — are called periodontal disease. Red, swollen gums, bleeding gums or loose teeth are all alarm signals for periodontal disease.

TOYOFUKU: Is this different from pyorrhea?

SATO: Pyorrhea is an advanced stage of periodontal disease in which pus accumulates in the gums. It is a type of periodontitis and can be a very serious disease. A milder, less threatening form of periodontitis is gingivitis (inflammation of the gums).

PRESIDENT IKEDA: The names are all so technical, it is confusing!

SATO: Yes, you are right there.

PRESIDENT IKEDA: Well, since this is such an important topic, I will do my best to keep up with you. Now let me see — pyorrhea is more serious than gingivitis. Is that right?

SATO: Yes. Gingivitis is caused by a bacterial infection of the gums. They bleed and swell up, but in most cases, once the plaque in which the bacteria live is removed, they heal.

MORITA: So, gingivitis is not such a serious condition?

SATO: Almost everyone has a touch of gingivitis, so one should not worry about it too much. But if it is allowed to go unchecked, there is cause for serious concern. There is a groove between the tooth and the gums. If gingivitis goes unchecked, bacteria begin to grow in it.

PRESIDENT IKEDA: It becomes like a pocket of bacteria.

SATO: Yes. In fact, it is even called a periodontal pocket. When it gets worse, the pocket gets deeper, and it eventually destroys the base that supports the tooth. This is periodontitis. (The periodontal membrane and alveolar bone that support the tooth are destroyed.)

MORITA: Are these conditions painful?

SATO: Unlike cavities, in most cases these conditions are not painful. As a result, they can grow worse without one's being aware of it. There are cases in which the person has never had a cavity, and then suddenly at about thirty-five, all the teeth are loosened and they have to be pulled.

> A clean, fresh mouth often says much about a person's character and pride in themselves, and the kind of impression he or she will create on others. People who must speak in public, at any rate, cannot afford to ignore dental hygiene. Brushing one's teeth is basic etiquette towards other people. Dental hygiene is an essential part of manners.

Dental Hygiene is the Top Priority

PRESIDENT IKEDA: Are these diseases caused by failure to keep the mouth and teeth clean?

SATO: Yes. They are caused by lack of proper hygiene. It is like failing to take a bath.

PRESIDENT IKEDA: A clean, fresh mouth often says much about a person's character and pride in themselves, and the kind of impression he or she will create on others. People who must speak in public, at any rate, cannot afford to ignore dental hygiene. Brushing one's teeth is basic etiquette towards other people. Dental hygiene is an essential part of manners.

SATO: How true! The only way to prevent periodontal disease is, as you might expect, brushing one's teeth. The important thing in brushing is to remove all plaque. When one allows plaque to remain in one's teeth, it hardens into a calcified material known as tartar. Tartar is too hard to remove by oneself.

Brushing Teeth Thoroughly at Least Once a Day

PRESIDENT IKEDA: How many times a day should one brush one's teeth?

SATO: Ideally, after every meal. But one does not really have to brush three times a day.

MORITA: Really? I am sure busy people will be very interested to hear more about this.

SATO: The fact is that even when you eat something sweet it does not turn into a cavity immediately. About twenty-four hours are required for plaque — the breeding ground of bacteria — to form.

PRESIDENT IKEDA: I see. So, as long as we remove the plaque within twenty-four hours, we are safe. That is wonderful news for people who hate to brush their teeth!

TOYOFUKU: On the other hand, we can look at it as encouragement to really brush our teeth thoroughly, even if it's only once a day.

SATO: I think that is the best viewpoint. Frequency of brushing isn't as important as the way we brush. The average Japanese brushes his or her teeth for only thirty seconds. That is not long enough to get rid of plaque. If one brushes one's teeth correctly, it should take about ten minutes.

PRESIDENT IKEDA: That is hard work, isn't it!

SATO: Yes, it is. It does take some getting used to, but if you brush correctly, you will be astonished at how clean you can get your teeth.

TOYOFUKU: When you spend so much time brushing your teeth, you won't want to get them dirty again, so you will avoid snacks and lose weight, too.

PRESIDENT IKEDA: There are all sorts of new gadgets for cleaning one's teeth, aren't there? But cleaning them carefully yourself is satisfying and, in the end, enjoyable. It also increases one's awareness of the importance of dental hygiene and protecting one's health in general.

MORITA: Yes. And, an added benefit is that activities requiring manual dexterity also develop our mental powers and prevent senility.

PRESIDENT IKEDA: That is wonderful. Can one brush one's teeth too much?

SATO: Some people damage their gums when brushing. Men, in particular, tend to brush too forcefully. It is best to hold one's toothbrush between the thumb and forefinger. Their combined pressure is just about right for brushing the teeth.

The Toothbrushes of Sakyamuni's Day

PRESIDENT IKEDA: The Buddhist scriptures speak of the benefits of keeping the mouth clean. They say it: (1) eliminates bad breath; (2) improves the sense of taste; (3) removes fever and phlegm in the mouth; and (4) stimulates the appetite.[1]

SATO: Were there toothbrushes in Sakyamuni's day?

PRESIDENT IKEDA: There was something called a 'tooth twig' (Skt *dantakastha*). This tooth twig was a small, pliant length of a twig cut from a tree. When one chewed it, the sap helped clean the teeth and the end of the twig was crushed into rough fibrous strands, much like a brush. Sakyamuni prescribed a particular length for this tooth cleaning twig, so that it would not poke the throats of his disciples.

MORITA: He really paid attention to the smallest details, didn't he?

PRESIDENT IKEDA: That is how concerned he was about his disciples' health.

---

1. Contained in the *Shibun Ritsu* (The Fourfold Rules of Discipline). The *vinaya* or monastic rules of the Dharmagupta School, translated from Sanskrit into Chinese by Buddhayashas.

Leaders must be concerned about details. When a meeting has been called, the leaders must be sensitive to every need of those who are attending: Are they tired, are they hungry? And when necessary, they should cut the meeting short so that everyone can go home and rest. Genuine leaders do not think of themselves; they base everything on the needs of those they serve.

A Small Amount of Toothpaste is Sufficient

PRESIDENT IKEDA: How frequently should we replace our toothbrush?

MORITA: Yes, it seems like some people have a favourite toothbrush that they hold on to for a long time.

SATO: Brushing with an old brush only undermines the purpose of hygiene! Generally, you should buy a new toothbrush about once a month. Once the bristles are a bit splayed, you can no longer brush correctly. It is important to replace one's toothbrush regularly to ensure proper dental hygiene. Brushes for between the teeth and dental floss are also very useful as supplemental care.

PRESIDENT IKEDA: How much toothpaste should one use when brushing? I think some people feel as if they have not brushed their teeth unless they are foaming at the mouth.

SATO: A little toothpaste is enough. It may feel good to use a lot, but it may lead you to think you have brushed your teeth carefully when in fact you have not done a thorough job.

TOYOFUKU: Recently, toothpastes with all kinds of enzymes and added ingredients are on sale.

SATO: Yes, there are many more varieties of late. But it is important to remember that toothpaste is just a supplement to brushing. The important thing is to brush your teeth and clean away the plaque.

Brush Each Tooth at Least Ten Times

PRESIDENT IKEDA: What is the best way to brush to get rid of plaque?

SATO: First, one should set the toothbrush at a right angle to the outside surface of the teeth *(see Figure 1)*. With very little movement of the wrist, move the brush back and forth horizontally *(see Figure 2)*. You should brush each tooth in this manner from ten to twenty times.

Brushing the inner side of the teeth, you should hold the brush at a 45-degree angle to the teeth *(see Figure 1)*. Then brush horizontally, just as you did the exterior surface.

TOYOFUKU: Until one gets the hang of it, it is probably a good idea to brush in front of a mirror. That way you can see how the brush is situated with respect to the teeth.

SATO: The bristles of a toothbrush are divided into 'toe' bristles, the 'side' bristles, and the 'heel' bristles *(see Figure 3)*. It is important to learn how to use each of these sections of bristles according to the tooth being brushed. For example, when you are using the 'toe' bristles to brush between your molars, the 'side' bristles can be used to brush in a vertical motion those places where the teeth may overlap slightly. Or when you brush the interior of your front teeth, you should place the 'heel' bristles at the gum line and brush upwards towards the cutting edge of the tooth *(see Figure 4)*.

TOYOFUKU: There are many different brushing techniques, aren't there?

Incidentally, if cavities and periodontal diseases are left unchecked, they can lead to endocarditis (an inflammation of the heart lining).

MORITA: People who suffer from such disorders as high blood pressure, coronary heart disease or diabetes should take special care when having dental work done. They should always discuss their medical conditions with their dentist first.

The Lotus Sutra Promises Beautiful Teeth

PRESIDENT IKEDA: The Lotus Sutra tells us that one of the benefits of listening to the teaching of the Mystic Law is healthy teeth.

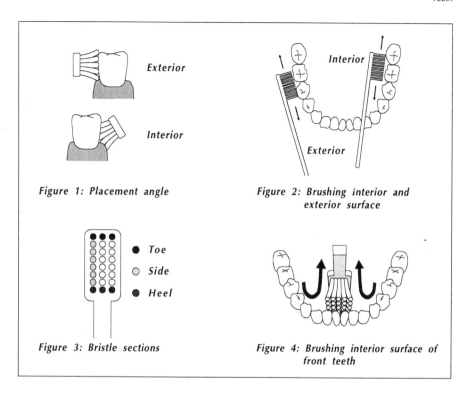

Figure 1: Placement angle

Figure 2: Brushing interior and exterior surface

Figure 3: Bristle sections

Figure 4: Brushing interior surface of front teeth

The Lotus Sutra states that a person who goes and listens to the sutra for even an instant will enjoy many physical benefits. Among these are listed: "His teeth will not be stained or black, nor will they be yellow or widely space, nor will they be missing or fall out or be at an angle or be crooked." (LS18, 248)[2]

Based on the Lotus Sutra, Soka Gakkai 2nd president Josei Toda stressed that these and other physical benefits accrue to those who propagate the True Law. He said: "The Lotus Sutra says that a person will be healthy, in fine

---

2. *The Lotus Sutra*, Burton Watson, chapter 18, pg 248.

form and condition. The description it contains offers documentary proof that believing in the Gohonzon will cure illness. And indeed, it is a fact that people with pure and sincere faith manifest a greatly improved facial appearance."[3]

That is certainly true. A person's face tells a lot about him or her, and the mouth and teeth are main focuses of attention in anyone's face. The Chinese poet, Du Fu (712-770), said of the legendary Tang dynasty beauty, Yang Guifei, "Her eyes are clear and her teeth white." Teeth have always been a point of attention, it seems.

MORITA: When you look at Western magazines, the people on the cover always have beautiful teeth.

PRESIDENT IKEDA: Japanese really have to improve their awareness of teeth and dental hygiene.

When all is said and done, each of us is responsible for our own health. And, healthy teeth are strongly linked to a healthy mind and body, and a long and happy life. We all need to continue brushing our teeth in the proper way so that we can have beautiful smiles that delight the hearts of all those we meet.

---

3. Josei Toda, *Toda Josei Zenshu* (Collected Writings of Josei Toda) (Tokyo: Seikyo Shimbunsha, 1983), vol III, pg 156.

Staying Healthy in Summer

Participants in this discussion on
' Humanism and the Art of Medicine:
A New Century of Health'
are SGI President Ikeda, Soka Gakkai
Doctors' Division Leaders Dr Shuhei Morita
and Dr Hiroyuki Toyofuku

MORITA: President Ikeda, I am sure you must be very tired after your long trip to the United States and countries of Central America. Your visit was a truly significant one in terms of building new bridges of understanding among different nations.

PRESIDENT IKEDA: Thank you. I am extremely grateful to all the SGI members around the world, whose prayers ensured the great success of my trip, the focus of which was on cultural and educational exchange.

TOYOFUKU: I understand this series on health is also being very well received by SGI members outside of Japan. It is being featured in the journals and publications of SGI organisations around the globe, and is widely read by both members and non-members alike.

PRESIDENT IKEDA: Yes, that is so. Everyone seems to be looking forward to the next discussion. Let us continue our discussions in the hope that they will help our friends the world over lead healthier and more fulfilling lives.

MORITA: Yes, let's!

TOYOFUKU: I couldn't agree more!

MORITA: The rainy season is forecast to come to an end in the Kanto region[1] towards the middle of July. Then, the hot weather will really start in earnest. I think the subject of staying healthy in summer would be an excellent choice for today's instalment.

PRESIDENT IKEDA: All right. Summer in Japan is especially hot and humid. Yet, all our members continue with their activities in spite of the heat. This is truly admirable.

TOYOFUKU: It is easy to get physically run down in the summer. Summer is also the peak season for food poisoning. Some sixty per cent of all food poisoning cases in Japan occur each year in the period from July to September.

---

1. Kanto region: The central area of the largest of Japan's four main islands, Honshu. The Kanto region comprises Kanagawa, Saitama, Chiba, Tochigi, Gumma and Ibaragi prefectures and the Tokyo Metropolitan Area.

Serious Food Poisoning Outbreak in Japan

PRESIDENT IKEDA: I heard that while I was overseas there was a serious outbreak of food poisoning in Japan.

MORITA: Yes, it was caused by the dangerous toxin-producing bacteria *E coli* 0157[2].

PRESIDENT IKEDA: What are some of the causes of food poisoning?

TOYOFUKU: Bacterial causes are by far the most frequent. They account for about seventy per cent of the cases. *E coli* 0157 belongs to this category.

Other causes include naturally occurring poisons, such as those found in certain varieties of mushrooms and blow fish (*fugu*), and the chemical poisons, such as mercury or arsenic.

PRESIDENT IKEDA: How many types of bacteria can cause food poisoning?

MORITA: They can be divided roughly into ten varieties.

Keep the Cutting Board Clean!

PRESIDENT IKEDA: How can we protect against them?

MORITA: The most important thing is cleanliness. It is important to wash our hands thoroughly before touching or preparing food.

TOYOFUKU: The bacteria, *Staphylococcus aureus*, a common cause of food poisoning, can be found almost anywhere on our skin, especially concentrating in our throats and noses, or around cuts.

PRESIDENT IKEDA: It is important that we wash our hands and gargle when we come in from being outdoors, isn't it? But not many people actually do so. In the sutras, Sakyamuni, too, teaches his followers to wash their hands and

---

2. *E coli* 0157: Full name is *Escherichia coli* 0157: H7. Causes haemorrhagic diarrhoea and has been linked with undercooked meat.

rinse their mouths before eating.[3]

Of course, it is not a good idea to get too fixated on this. If we become obsessed with germs, we will even be afraid to breathe!

TOYOFUKU: And, we certainly won't live long then! But joke aside, I think it is a good idea, for example, to wear a gauze mask[4] when cooking if we have a cold.

MORITA: We should also be careful to thoroughly wash the cutting board, knives and kitchen utensils we use, and also any towels and wipe-up cloths that are used in the kitchen. The bacteria, *Vibrio parahaemolyticus*, which is another common cause of food poisoning in summer, is found on the gills and scales of fish. It is easy to pass this bacteria from one food to another if one does not clean the cutting board.

Toxins Produced by Bacteria can be Impervious to Heat

PRESIDENT IKEDA: I see. Is it best after all to avoid eating perishables and uncooked foods, such as raw fish and the like, in summer?

TOYOFUKU: Yes, probably. The safest thing is to grill or boil such foods thoroughly, so that they are well-cooked all the way through.

PRESIDENT IKEDA: Does heating foods sufficiently make them safe?

MORITA: Most bacteria are killed by cooking temperatures. But we must remember that, in some cases, even if we kill the bacteria by heating the food, the toxins produced by the bacteria can still cause food poisoning.

TOYOFUKU: *Staphylococcus aureus* is quickly killed by heat, for example, but the enterotoxins the bacteria produced are not easily destroyed by heating.

---

3. Contained in the *Shibun Ritsu* (The Fourfold Rules of Discipline). The *vinaya* or monastic rules of the Dharmagupta school, translated from Sanskrit into Chinese by Buddhayashas.
4. Gauze mask worn over the nose and mouth to help prevent the spread of infectious viruses.

PRESIDENT IKEDA: "A tiger dies and leaves its skin," as the saying goes. In the same way, it seems, bacteria dies but leaves behind its poison. We cannot be too careful, can we?

MORITA: That is right. In such cases, no amount of grilling or boiling will help.

Keep the Refrigerator Clean and Organised

PRESIDENT IKEDA: Sometimes we buy more than we need because we think it will keep if we put it in the refrigerator.

TOYOFUKU: Yes. But when we pack too much into our refrigerator, the air circulation is restricted and the temperature rises.

PRESIDENT IKEDA: Making it easier for bacteria to multiply?

MORITA: Exactly. We should try to remember that foods do not keep as long in summer as they do in other seasons. It is not good to place too much faith in our refrigerator. The internal temperature can also rise if we open and close the door too frequently.

TOYOFUKU: It is also important to remember to always keep the refrigerator clean and well organised inside. Foremost, we should never leave any food in the refrigerator for too long.

PRESIDENT IKEDA: Is there a way to tell for certain whether food in the refrigerator has spoiled?

MORITA: Not really. In fact, there are some foods that may still smell and look fresh but can cause food poisoning if ingested. If a certain type of food smells odd when you heat it, there is a good chance that it has already spoiled.

Bacteria can Even Survive in Vacuum Packs!

TOYOFUKU: The same is true of vacuum-packed foods. Among the bacteria that cause food poisoning are those that live and produce toxins in environments where there is no oxygen. If there is a strange smell when you open the pack, the food should not be eaten under any circumstances.

PRESIDENT IKEDA: People who love to eat have to stay on their toes in the summer, don't they!

> **Seriously, the attitude, "just a little bit won't hurt," can cause big problems later on. Nichiren Daishonin writes, "Prudent caution must always be taken in the depths of your heart." Anyone who naively thinks that one does not have to worry about food poisoning because one is practising the Daishonin's Buddhism is simply being complacent and demonstrating an erroneous attitude towards faith.**

Seriously, the attitude, "just a little bit won't hurt," can cause big problems later on. Nichiren Daishonin writes, "Prudent caution must always be taken in the depths of your heart." (*Gosho Zenshu*, pg 1176) Anyone who naively thinks that one does not have to worry about food poisoning because one is practising the Daishonin's Buddhism is simply being complacent and demonstrating an erroneous attitude towards faith.

It would be wise for us to remember to be very careful about what we eat in summer.

TOYOFUKU: Yes. The key to avoiding food poisoning is to select fresh foods and use them quickly.

Sakyamuni was Stricken by Food Poisoning

PRESIDENT IKEDA: Incidentally, it is said that Sakyamuni was stricken with a severe attack of food poisoning before he died.

TOYOFUKU: What did he eat?

PRESIDENT IKEDA: One account[5] says that he ate some truffles[6]. The aged Sakyamuni stopped in a mango grove hut which was owned by a follower named Chunda, the son of a copper-smith. Chunda was deeply impressed with Sakyamuni's teachings and begged him to join his family for a meal. Sakyamuni silently agreed. Chunda prepared a great delicacy for his honoured guest, a dish containing truffles.

The Buddha preached the Law to Chunda, then ate the food. Shortly afterwards, Sakyamuni was stricken with sharp stomach pains and a severe bloody diarrhoea. The diarrhoea weakened him greatly and eventually caused his death. But as he lay dying, Sakyamuni said to his disciple, Ananda: "Someone may cause Chunda to regret the offering he made to me, by saying, 'Chunda, Sakyamuni ate the food you gave him and then he died. Therefore, there is no merit in your offering.' So please, this is what you must say to Chunda: 'Chunda, my friend, the food you gave to Sakyamuni helped him enter a wonderful nirvana. Thus, my friend, your offering has far more merit than that of any other offering of food.'"

This story is a fine example of the spirit of Buddhism. Though Sakyamuni was suffering from the pains of illness, he worried about another and extended a compassionate hand to relieve his suffering. Doesn't this signify what a healthy life should be in the truest sense of the word?

Two Weeks to Adapt to Summer

PRESIDENT IKEDA: To return to our topic of staying healthy in summer, let us talk about the summer fatigue syndrome that plagues many people in Japan at this time of the year.

MORITA: But, we do not necessarily suffer from fatigue just because the weather is very hot. Human beings have a natural capacity to adapt to their environment.

TOYOFUKU: It is said to take the body about two weeks to acclimatise itself to summer weather conditions.

---

5. cf 'Maha Paranibbana Suttanta' in *Dialogues of the Buddha*, translated from the Pali of the Digha Nikaya by T W and C A F Rhys Davids (Oxford: The Pali Text Society, 1995), part 2, pg 137-147.
6. Truffles: A type of edible subterranean fungi prized as a great delicacy from ancient times.

PRESIDENT IKEDA: So, one important point is to prepare our body so that it can withstand the summer heat.

MORITA: Yes. The basic strategies are a balanced diet, sufficient sleep and moderate exercise.

PRESIDENT IKEDA: It is quite common to lose one's appetite when it gets hot.

TOYOFUKU: Yes, it is the perfect season for dieting! But we must watch out that our diet does not become nutritionally imbalanced. When it is hot, many Japanese favour light, very plain foods, such as cold noodles or rice gruel, and it is easy not to get enough protein, vitamins and minerals.

PRESIDENT IKEDA: The traditional Japanese dish for stamina in the summer is charcoal broiled eel.

TOYOFUKU: Yes, eating eel in the summer is a good custom. The animal protein it provides can help replenish our strength in summer's enervating weather.

PRESIDENT IKEDA: But when you are not very hungry, it is hard to eat something as rich as broiled eel.

MORITA: Lately, it is has gone so expensive that many of us cannot eat it even if we wanted to!

TOYOFUKU: In that case, I would like to recommend a cold tofu dish. Soybean, from which tofu is made, is an excellent source of vegetable protein.

PRESIDENT IKEDA: It is cool and easy to swallow, and it is not expensive, either.

MORITA: Vinegar can also help stimulate the appetite, and it has germicidal qualities as well.

PRESIDENT IKEDA: What should we do to make sure we do not become dehydrated in the summer?

TOYOFUKU: Drink plenty of water or green tea, but avoid drinking carbonated soft drinks every time you are thirsty or you will end up consuming too much sugar and losing your appetite for nutritious foods.

Napping to Beat the Heat

PRESIDENT IKEDA: When it is really hot, it can be hard to sleep at night, and we find ourselves feeling tired from lack of sleep.

TOYOFUKU: That is right. Researchers say that if people could get a good night's sleep as part of their regular daily routine, half the problem of summer fatigue would be solved.

MORITA: Insufficient sleep and an irregular daily schedule weaken the immune system and make us feel listless. In summer, it is a good idea to go to sleep earlier than usual and to try to wake up early.

PRESIDENT IKEDA: In summer, we should be especially careful to get enough sleep each night so that we can start the new day fully refreshed. Those who are older might find it helpful to take an afternoon nap if they still feel tired the next day. A brief nap can do wonders for restoring one's energy. The important thing is not to allow exhaustion to accumulate. We need to have the wisdom to get enough sleep. Are there any particular techniques for getting a good night's sleep?

MORITA: It can help to take a shower or bath just before bedtime, so one feels clean and refreshed. Light cotton night clothes allow for good ventilation and absorb perspiration well.

TOYOFUKU: Working up a good, healthy sweat is one of the barometers of summer health. Moderate exercise improves blood circulation and is effective in overcoming fatigue.

MORITA: You could give yourself a dry-towel rub, or do a short programme of calisthenics, take a walk, or do some other form of light exercise in the cooler hours of the morning or evening. Or, you could leave for work a little earlier than usual and walk to one train station further along the line from the one you usually use.

PRESIDENT IKEDA: The way we start the morning is very important in terms of the satisfaction we get out of each day. Victory in the morning means a victory for the whole day. If we repeat that process daily, our whole life will be victorious.

I believe it was the German poet, Goethe, who called morning 'the golden hours'. Most of us work better at this time of the day, too. I think we should all try to get off to a good start each morning. And, of course, for us in the SGI, the key to a good start is morning *gongyo*.[7]

Keep the Air-conditioning at 27-28 Degrees Centigrade

PRESIDENT IKEDA: Air-conditioning set at too cold a temperature is another prime cause of illness or various complaints and ailments during summer, isn't it?

TOYOFUKU: Yes, indeed. As a result of going frequently back and forth from the heat outside to the cool inside during the summer months, many Japanese catch chills and suffer from stomach cramps and diarrhoea.

MORITA: It can bring on an overall feeling of lethargy and sluggishness, and cause women's menstrual cycles to become irregular. These are symptoms of the so-called air-conditioning syndrome.

PRESIDENT IKEDA: What is the proper temperature for air-conditioning in summer?

MORITA: We should keep our homes at about 27 or 28 degrees centigrade, while the workplace should not drop below 25. The temperatures at which different people feel comfortable vary, but when the gap between the outside and inside temperatures is too extreme, it can only cause harm.

PRESIDENT IKEDA: It is important to think carefully about the proper temperature in halls and auditoriums where large numbers of people are gathering. We cannot simply turn up the air-conditioning because it is hot outside. We must never forget those who are especially susceptible to chills, such as women, whose body temperatures tend to be lower than men, and those who may be feeling unwell or who are in poor physical health.

---

7. *Gongyo*: Literally, *assiduous practice*. In Nichiren Daishonin's Buddhism, *gongyo* consists of reciting excerpts from the 2nd and 16th chapters of the Lotus Sutra and chanting Nam-myoho-renge-kyo.

Always Carry a Summer Jacket or Sweater

MORITA: It is always a good idea to carry a jacket or a cardigan along with you to protect yourself from the cold blasts of the air-conditioning.

PRESIDENT IKEDA: That is right. One extra layer can protect against sharp differences in temperature.

TOYOFUKU: It is easy to catch a summer cold if we are repeatedly going from sweating profusely to being exposed to the chill of air-conditioning. Summer colds are marked by lethargy, a runny nose, headache, stiff neck and shoulder muscles and gastrointestinal problems. When we work up a sweat in summer and are drenched through, it is important that we change promptly into dry clothes.

MORITA: I recommend taking to work a jacket to' throw over your shoulders or a blanket for your lap and to use them to prevent your shoulders or feet, as the case may be, from getting too chilled.

PRESIDENT IKEDA: There are many traditional items and devices that have been designed, especially for getting through Japan's hot, muggy summers, aren't there? Such things as bamboo or wooden benches on which to sit outdoors, the light cotton kimono called *yukata*, the sprinkling of walkways and paths with water to cool them, and reed blinds that allow abundant ventilation while screening out the sun. All were born out of the wisdom and ingenuity of daily life to make the best possible use of any cool summer breezes.

We need wisdom for both health and happiness. Nichiren Daishonin writes, "The five characters of the *daimoku* [Nam-myoho-renge-kyo] become . . . a cool breeze in the hell of burning heat." (*Gosho Zenshu*, pg 822) Of course, the Daishonin is not talking about hot weather, but it remains true that a life based on the Mystic Law will give us the life force to endure the summer heat. Wisdom is included in that life force. Life force means living wisely.

We want to live each day in the best of health and spirits, managing our physical well-being as skilfully as a master pilot flies an aeroplane.

Emergency First Aid

Participants in this discussion on
' Humanism and the Art of Medicine:
A New Century of Health'
are SGI President Ikeda, Soka Gakkai
Doctors' Division Leaders Dr Shuhei Morita
and Dr Hiroyuki Toyofuku

President Ikeda: At last, summer is really here. Schools are out and many families will be heading to places, such as the mountains or the beach.

Morita: Contact with nature helps relieve stress and refreshes us.

Toyofuku: The down side of this season is that there is an increase in accidents at these various vacation spots as well as traffic accidents, as more people are on the road.

President Ikeda: Yes, that is true. When we relax and let our guard down, accidents are likely to happen. An important way to prevent accidents is to remain alert and consciously decide you will not allow an accident to happen. A firm, conscious decision to avoid accidents actually works like a protective barrier against their occurrence.

The Minutes Before the Ambulance Arrives are Crucial

Morita: Yes. But to be prepared for any situation, let us discuss emergency first-aid treatment in this instalment.

President Ikeda: Yes, that is important. The difference between knowing and not knowing what to do in an emergency situation can be crucial.

Morita: Indeed. Brain damage occurs after a person has stopped breathing for about ten minutes, and only about three or five minutes after the heart has stopped beating.

Toyofuku: That is why the assistance we give a victim of sudden injury or illness before the ambulance arrives is so important.

President Ikeda: Yes, those minutes can mean the difference between life and death.

Morita: That is true. And there is still a lot of room for improvement in Japan's emergency medical system, too.

President Ikeda: I have heard that in the West, most citizens have a basic grounding in emergency first aid. It is taken quite seriously. Nichiren Daishonin has said, "Life is the most precious of all treasures." (*WND*, pg 955) Society as a whole must make a more serious commitment to protecting and saving precious human lives. And to promote awareness in that direction, steps should be taken to ensure that every citizen is familiar with basic skills in first aid.

Check for Consciousness, Breathing and Pulse

PRESIDENT IKEDA: What is the first step to take in an emergency situation, such as an accident or sudden illness?

TOYOFUKU: First, we should check three things: Is the victim conscious? Is he breathing? Does he have a pulse? We start with whether the victim is conscious. Speak to the victim in a loud voice and watch the reaction. If the victim is conscious, he should reply or open his eyes.

MORITA: If there is no reaction, try lightly slapping the victim's cheek, or pinching it. If there is still no reaction, ask someone to call an ambulance immediately.

> Nichiren Daishonin has said, "Life is the most precious of all treasures." Society as a whole must make a more serious commitment to protecting and saving precious human lives. And to promote awareness in that direction, steps should be taken to ensure that every citizen is familiar with basic skills in first aid.

PRESIDENT IKEDA: Speed is of the essence, isn't it?

TOYOFUKU: It certainly is. If you do not act quickly, a life that could have been saved may be lost.

PRESIDENT IKEDA: In an emergency situation, a person's true character is revealed. Even though we may know that speedy action is important, when faced with an emergency we may not move quickly enough unless we are mentally prepared and helping others, and taking action for their welfare are second nature to us.

Morita: On that score, I think SGI members are well prepared.

Do Not Move the Victim

President Ikeda: Is it all right to touch a victim who had sudden serious injury or collapse?

Morita: Yes. But it is very important not to shake or move the person. Vigorous shaking can cause serious harm to a victim of stroke, for instance.

President Ikeda: I see. One can't be too careful. Without the proper knowledge of what to do in an emergency, one could cause irreversible harm.

Toyofuku: Yes. Because in such situations, people inadvertently tend to shake the victim forcefully to try to get him to respond.

President Ikeda: What should one do while waiting for the ambulance to arrive?

Morita: Determine whether the victim is breathing or not.

President Ikeda: How should one do that?

Morita: Place your ear near the victim's mouth and nose, and see if you can detect any breath. You can also watch the chest to see if it is moving up and down.

Toyofuku: If the person is breathing, just leave him in a comfortable resting position.

Resuscitation Methods

President Ikeda: If the victim is not breathing, do we perform artificial respiration?

Morita: First, look inside the victim's mouth. Sometimes when a person loses consciousness, the tongue falls back and blocks the airway in the throat.

TOYOFUKU: If you see that is the case, gently lift the victim's chin and tilt the head back, opening the airway. Raising the shoulders by placing something soft — a rolled-up jacket, for example — under them will help you carry this out smoothly.

MORITA: Then, begin the artificial respiration. Lightly pinch the victim's nostrils shut to keep air from escaping and blow a full breath of air into the victim's mouth for about two seconds. Then, check the victim's pulse.

PRESIDENT IKEDA: Where can the pulse be detected?

TOYOFUKU: One of the best places for checking the pulse is on the neck, right next to the Adam's apple.

MORITA: If there is no pulse, it is time to perform cardiopulmonary resuscitation (CPR), a combination of chest compressions and artificial respiration. Briefly, what the rescuer does is to place one hand on the victim's chest, aligning the base of his thumb slightly above the victim's solar plexus (the pit of the stomach), and then places the other hand on top of the first. Keeping his elbows straight, he then pushes straight down and compresses the victim's chest about four to five centimetres (one to two inches). [Editor's note: *This procedure should not be attempted without proper training.*]

PRESIDENT IKEDA: That sounds difficult. One needs training to do it right, I am sure.

TOYOFUKU: Yes. Then the rescuer repeats sets of fifteen chest compressions and two artificial respirations.

Stemming Bleeding

PRESIDENT IKEDA: What should be done when a victim is bleeding because of an injury?

MORITA: It is important to stop the bleeding right away. Light bleeding can be stopped by firmly pressing a clean handkerchief or towel on the wound.

PRESIDENT IKEDA: The sight of blood can be pretty alarming.

1. Check for any blockages
   lodged in the throat.

2. Perform artificial
   respiration.

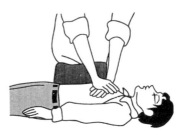

3. Apply chest compressions.

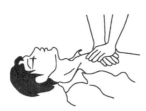

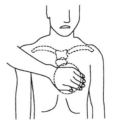

Hands crossed and placed on
top of the victim's chest.

Hand position on the
victim's chest.

MORITA: It is important to remain calm. Many people become alarmed and frightened in an emergency. But if you lose control, you won't be able to treat the victim properly.

PRESIDENT IKEDA: It seems to me that women are often braver than men when it comes to an emergency!

TOYOFUKU: Never use cotton wool to try to stem the bleeding or use rubber bands for a tourniquet. Dubious home remedies should also be avoided at all costs. Such materials and treatments are only likely to cause infection or nerve damage, as the case may be.

Wear a Hat Outdoors

PRESIDENT IKEDA: When outdoors for a long time exposed to the direct rays of the sun, one can experience dizziness, nausea and headache.

TOYOFUKU: Those are the symptoms of sunstroke. Another danger in the summer is heat-stroke, the result of overheating the body from staying too long in a hot or humid place.

MORITA: Heat-stroke is most likely to occur when there is poor circulation in a room, or when you are wearing clothes that do not allow your body heat to escape, or when you cannot sufficiently reduce your body heat through perspiration.

PRESIDENT IKEDA: What should be done for victim of sunstroke or heat-stroke?

TOYOFUKU: The first step is to lower the body temperature. Bring the victim to a cool, well-ventilated place and lay him down. Loosen the victim's clothing and fan him with a coat or whatever else is handy.

PRESIDENT IKEDA: One should, whenever possible, wear a hat when going outside in the summer.

MORITA: Yes. It is wise to avoid over-exposure to direct sunlight.

When outdoors for a long time exposed to the direct rays of the sun, one can experience dizziness, nausea and headache.

TOYOFUKU: Another tip is to wear loose-fitting, lightweight clothing that allows for good ventilation and does not trap in heat.

MORITA: If you perspire a lot, drink plenty of liquids, preferably those that contain some salt, like certain sports drinks, to replace the water and salt you lose as you perspire.

Never Leave Children Unattended in a Closed Car

PRESIDENT IKEDA: Every summer, we hear of cases in which children have died from heat-stroke because their parents left them in the car with the doors locked and windows closed. These are tragic, and completely preventable, accidents.

MORITA: Yes. We must never leave small children in the car when we go shopping or have some errand to run.

TOYOFUKU: A closed car becomes as hot as an oven in a very short space of time. There have also been cases in which parents have left children in closed cars with the engine running and the air-conditioning on, but when the engine went off while they were away, it led to tragic consequences. We have to be careful at all times.

President Ikeda: In anything and everything, the little things are what count. We must never overlook them. Nichiren Daishonin teaches us, "Though the embankment between rice fields is firm, if there is an ant hole in it, then surely, in the long run, it will never remain full of water." (*WND*, pg 626) Failing to pay attention to the little things leads to unexpected accidents.

Tanning Ages the Skin

Toyofuku: Another summer danger is excessive tanning.

President Ikeda: We think of a suntan as a sign of health, but the ultraviolet (UV) rays of the sun are harmful, aren't they?

Toyofuku: Yes. While a small amount of sunshine can be effective in killing bacteria on the skin, excessive exposure can cause burning and blistering and speed up the ageing of the skin, causing wrinkles and blotches.

President Ikeda: The sun is a natural enemy of youthful skin. How can we avoid overexposure to the sun?

Morita: If you are going outside when the sun is at its strongest, carry a sunshade, wear a hat, or apply sunscreen to your exposed skin.

Cool Minor Burns with Water

President Ikeda: What is the best treatment for burns other than sunburn?

Morita: When the burn is relatively minor, the first thing is to cool it with water. The best method is to place the burn area under cold running tap water for at least thirty minutes. Quick treatment of this kind — to cool the burn — can reduce the damage and speed the healing.[1]

---

1. When the burn is quite serious, immersing in water is not recommended.

TOYOFUKU: If the burn is covered by your clothing, run the water over the clothing. By attempting to remove the garment, you may peel off skin from the burned area and increase the chances of infection.

PRESIDENT IKEDA: The old-fashioned Japanese home remedy that was supposed to be good for a burn was to put *miso* (fermented soy-bean paste) or soy sauce on it.

TOYOFUKU: Yes, but those are very bad treatments. Never put *miso* or soy sauce on a burn. They are likely to cause infection and worsen the injury.

PRESIDENT IKEDA: We had better beware of so-called home remedies, hadn't we? Often there are accidents in the home where children are burned by scalding water or the steam from pots and pans on the stove and, especially here in Japan, from the steam escaping from the vent of the automatic electrical rice cookers.

MORITA: Any pots filled with boiling water and any heated appliances should be kept far out of children's reach.

Accidents in the Home

PRESIDENT IKEDA: We often think of accidents as taking place outside of the home, but we are not safe at home, either. They say that accidents in the home are the second largest cause of accidental deaths, surpassed only by traffic accidents.

TOYOFUKU: Many people do not know that, but it is true. We need to be especially careful when there are children or elderly people in the family.

MORITA: Common household accidents — such as falling down the stairs, ingesting some foreign object or food and choking on it, or drowning in the bath — often claim children and the elderly.

PRESIDENT IKEDA: If we grow complacent and think that nothing can happen to us at home, accidents that could have been easily prevented are more likely to occur. The Daishonin says, "A wise person, while dwelling in security, anticipates danger; a perverse one, while dwelling amid danger, takes security for granted." (*WND*, pg 621) Just a little bit of care, of caution, can make all the difference in the world. It can turn the path of one's life around 180 degrees. We must act with wisdom and prudence. In order to properly carry out our mission in life, we must shine a spotlight on every corner of our lives, to make sure we are safe and secure. We must not allow ourselves to slip into a careless pattern of making do, getting by, and putting off. Many of us are over-confident of our strength and overdo it during the summer months. Most accidents can be traced to fatigue and carelessness. I hope that all of our readers will, based on their fervent prayers and the determination to manifest faith in daily life, live wisely this summer, so that they can look back later and say it was a truly worthwhile and enjoyable summer.

Children's Health

Participants in this discussion on
' Humanism and the Art of Medicine:
A New Century of Health'
are SGI President Ikeda, Soka Gakkai
Doctors' Division Leaders Dr Shuhei Morita
and Dr Hiroyuki Toyofuku

Morita: Now that school is out for the summer, there are more opportunities for parents to spend time with their children. With this closer contact, some parents may notice health problems in their children, that under normal circumstances they might overlook. I think this is an excellent opportunity for us to discuss children's health.

President Ikeda: I agree. It has often been noted that children aren't simply the 'little adults'. But does this apply to their health as well? Are the illnesses that afflict children different from those that afflict adults?

Toyofuku: There are distinct differences between adults and children in the way symptoms manifest themselves and in the progress of diseases. Nor can we lump all the children together. There is a considerable difference between a one-month-old baby and an elementary schoolchild. There are also individual differences to consider.

President Ikeda: I see. They say that there are as many surprises as there are children and I guess we can also say there are as many diseases as there are children, too!

Morita: That is by no means an exaggeration. The biggest difference between childhood and adult diseases is that children's diseases can have an effect on their growth and development.

President Ikeda: They can affect a child's whole life, can't they? That is why taking good care of children's health is so important. Parents around the world share a universal prayer that their children may grow up strong and healthy.

Fever Assists in Fighting Disease

President Ikeda: Children frequently run fever. What is the reason for this?

Morita: Children are always touching things around them and putting them in their mouths. You might say they are veritably eating viruses and bacteria! Picking up something in this way is the most common cause of fevers in children. Generally speaking, however, it is not necessary to try to lower a child's fever in every case. There is no relationship between how high a

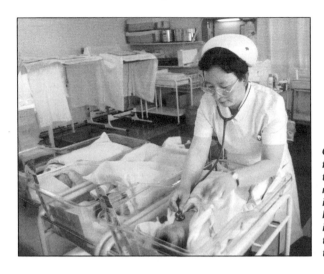

Children frequently run fever. A fever is one of the body's defence mechanisms against invading viruses or bacteria. It activates the immune system, increasing the body's natural ability to fight the virus.

fever is and how serious an illness is.

TOYOFUKU: A fever is one of the body's defence mechanisms against invading viruses or bacteria. It activates the immune system, increasing the body's natural ability to fight the virus.

PRESIDENT IKEDA: A fever, then, is a sign that the body is fighting a virus.

MORITA: Yes. The body's defence system is said to work best at 39°C (102.2°F)[1] If the body temperature reaches over 40°C (104°F), the activity of the immune system is impaired.

PRESIDENT IKEDA: Can a high fever have any adverse effects on the brain?

MORITA: Though certain diseases of the brain, such as meningitis, do produce

---

1. To convert temperature from Celsius to Fahrenheit, multiply by 1.8 and add 32.

high fevers, having a high fever in itself generally doesn't harm the brain.

PRESIDENT IKEDA: That is a relief to know. When they simply have a slight fever, most children are out playing rather than resting. They are completely oblivious to any concern their parents might have about their health.

MORITA: Yes, it is a perfect case of a child not knowing a parent's heart. In any event, as long as the child seems well and energetic, there is no need to be overly worried, even if they are running a fever.

PRESIDENT IKEDA: What is the best way to accurately take a child's temperature?

TOYOFUKU: There are several methods commonly employed — inserting the thermometer under the arm, beneath the tongue, or in the rectum. In Japan, we most commonly place the thermometer under the arm.

First, wipe away any sweat from the underarm area, and then place the tip of the thermometer in the indentation under the arm. The thermometer will naturally rest at an angle; there is no need to keep it perfectly horizontal.

MORITA: Have the child place the arm straight down. With an infant, it is perfectly acceptable to hold the child in your arms, while you hold its arm down to keep the thermometer securely positioned. A mercury thermometer should be kept in place for about ten minutes; a digital thermometer, for one or two minutes.

PRESIDENT IKEDA: The temperature will be different depending upon when it is taken, won't it?

TOYOFUKU: Yes. After nursing or eating a meal, or after crying or playing, the temperature of an infant or child will be a bit higher than usual. It is best to wait for about ten minutes after any exertion or eating, or take the temperature before a meal or when the child is quiet. In addition, the body temperature is likely to be higher (by 0.5^{0}C to 1.0^{0}C [0.9^{0}F to 1.8^{0}F] in the evening, and a bit lower in the morning.

MORITA: The normal body temperature is also different from individual to individual, and further varies according to age. Learning one's normal temperature can be of use in monitoring one's health.

Give Plenty of Fluids to a Fevered Child

PRESIDENT IKEDA: What should parents do when a child runs a fever?

MORITA: Make sure to give the child plenty of fluids. It is said that some sixty per cent of the water in the body of a nursing infant is used up and replaced every day. Since this rate of water consumption is so high, a child who has a fevers or diarrhoea can quickly become dehydrated.

TOYOFUKU: The same is true when a child is healthy. Dehydration can also cause fevers.

PRESIDENT IKEDA: What kinds of fever should parents be especially concerned about?

TOYOFUKU: A fever over 40^{0}C (104^{0}F); a fever of over 39^{0}C (102.2^{0}F) that continues for more than three days; a fever accompanied by listlessness and inactivity; and any fever in an infant under three months of age. In any of these cases, the child should be taken to see a doctor quickly.

PRESIDENT IKEDA: Fevers in children are sometimes accompanied by convulsions.

TOYOFUKU: Yes. These are called febrile seizures. The child may stop breathing, the eyes may roll back in the sockets, the body may become rigid, and the child may lose consciousness. Such convulsions are quite common with a fever of over 38^{0}C (100.4^{0}F), and are most frequently seen in children aged six and under.

PRESIDENT IKEDA: What should a parent do when a child has such a convulsion?

TOYOFUKU: Loosen the child's clothes and lay the child down. If possible, turn the child's face to the side so that if the child should vomit something up, it won't block the child's throat. One should not shout, or shake, or jolt the child in any way.

MORITA: Some people place a towel or cloth between a convulsing child's teeth to prevent them from biting their tongue, but the towel can cause the child to gag and throw up. So, it is best not to place anything in the mouth.

PRESIDENT IKEDA: Is there anything else that should be done?

MORITA: First, do not panic. Stay calm and cool. There is a saying among paediatricians — when a child with convulsions is brought in, the first thing to do is take a cigarette break.

PRESIDENT IKEDA: What does that mean?

MORITA: Of course, it does not mean that the doctor really lights a cigarette and takes a smoking break. What it means is that most convulsions stop naturally within about five minutes.

PRESIDENT IKEDA: In other words, in the time it takes to smoke a cigarette.

MORITA: Yes. That is why parents should not panic when a child has febrile convulsions at home. Stay calm and watch over the child carefully. In most cases when the parent rushes the infant to the hospital, the child is peacefully sleeping by the time they get into the examination room.

TOYOFUKU: On the other hand, if the seizure lasts more than five minutes, one should take the child to see a doctor immediately. In all childhood illnesses, the parent's wise judgment and quick response are very important.

Jivaka, the Famous Physician of Sakyamuni's Day, was also a Paediatrician

PRESIDENT IKEDA: Speaking of paediatrics, it seems that this was a separate area within medicine as early as Sakyamuni's day. Of course, it was not a specialised medical field as it is today, but there are indications that the study and treatment of children's diseases were considered very important. Buddhist texts identify the famous doctor of Sakyamuni's day, Jivaka[2], as a great paediatrician. There is, of course, the well-known episode where Jivaka successfully operated on a child suffering from an intestinal blockage.[3]

---

2. Jivaka: A skilled physician of the kingdom of Magadha in ancient India.
3. This episode is contained in the *Shibun Ritsu* (The Fourfold Rules of Discipline), the *vinaya* or monastic rules of the Dharmagupta School translated from Sanskrit into Chinese by Buddhayashas.

For parents, the best way to handle bed-wetting is: Don't get angry, don't wake the child, don't worry about it. They should make efforts to allow the child to relax, sleep well and get up early.

Be Patient with Bed-wetting

PRESIDENT IKEDA: I am sure there are many parents among our readers who are concerned about their child's bed-wetting.

MORITA: Yes, no doubt there are. But there is really no need to worry too much about it. It takes most children until about the age of five to gain proper control of their urination. When a child who has reached elementary school age still wets the bed regularly, there can be several causes, and it is hard to pinpoint one.

TOYOFUKU: There is some evidence that overly strict toilet training can become a psychological cause of bed-wetting.

PRESIDENT IKEDA: Is there any cure for this disorder?

TOYOFUKU: Unfortunately, there is no magic formula. When bed-wetting is caused by physical problems, such as disorders of the urinary tract or a hormone imbalance, it can be treated medically. But it is important to note that scolding the child will not cure bed-wetting.

MORITA: For parents, the best way to handle the situation is: Don't get angry, don't wake the child, don't worry about it. They should make efforts to allow the child to relax, sleep well and get up early.

PRESIDENT IKEDA: I see. I know that parents may be concerned about this problem, but they should take comfort in knowing that children who wet their beds exist the world over, and almost all of them grow out of it eventually. Perhaps the best way to 'cure' bed-wetting is to take a patient, long-term view towards it and not fret about it too much.

A Sense of Security can also Cure Speech Impediments

TOYOFUKU: Yes. Too much scolding on the part of parents can also cause their children to suffer from a host of other problems, such as speech impediments.

PRESIDENT IKEDA: That is another thing that concerns parents.

MORITA: And, it is another example of a behaviour that cannot be cured by scolding. If anything, scolding a child about a speech problem usually only makes it worse.

PRESIDENT IKEDA: One often sees parents who talk to their children in a manner that resembles the rapid fire of a machine gun: "What?" "Well?" "Hurry up!" Not just children, but anyone subjected to such an impatient and unrelenting barrages would start to stutter!

TOYOFUKU: Speaking slowly and listening carefully and patiently to a stuttering child will almost always solve the problem.

PRESIDENT IKEDA: The key point in treating such behaviour is making the child feel secure, right?

MORITA: Yes. Not only in the case of speech impediments but in all children's health problems, the parent responsible for the child's daily welfare can play a major part in diagnosis and healing. There are many cases when a parent intuitively senses that something is not quite the same as usual with their child, and a serious illness is subsequently diagnosed. The parent who is with the child everyday knows the child's condition far better than any doctor can.

PRESIDENT IKEDA: I heard the following anecdote from members of the Shirakaba-kai (the Soka Gakkai Women's Division nurses' group). It is the story of a mother who wouldn't give up on her daughter, who had fallen into a coma after an automobile accident.

The doctors gave the girl no chance of recovery. But her mother never lost hope; she was certain her daughter would recover. She stayed by her daughter's side day after day, stroking her body and speaking encouraging words to her. "Good morning!" "Does it hurt?" "Just be patient a little longer." She kept up a steady flow of soft, loving words. She also hung up a tangerine — a fruit produced in their hometown — over her daughter's head and held the girl's hand up to touch it from time to time. She wanted it to be the first thing her daughter saw when she regained consciousness — such was her love.

TOYOFUKU: Nothing can beat a mother's love.

PRESIDENT IKEDA: About a month after the accident, as the mother was speaking to her daughter as always, tears suddenly welled up in the girl's eyes. The mother urged, "Give it your best effort!" and soon her daughter's tears were flowing freely. She had regained consciousness. Afterwards, with the warm encouragement of her mother, the daughter regained the use of one part of her body after another.

A parent's encouragement is more powerful than any medicine. For a child, a parent is the best doctor. That is why I hope that all parents will acquire correct health information and the wisdom to use it properly.

A parent's encouragement is more powerful than any medicine. For a child, a parent is the best doctor. That is why I hope that all parents will acquire correct health information and the wisdom to use it properly.

Balanced Diet and Exercise are also Essential for Children

PRESIDENT IKEDA: We hear recently that children are beginning to succumb to adult illnesses.

TOYOFUKU: Yes, we are seeing illnesses, such as diabetes and high blood pressure in children.

Children are a mirror that reflect the state of society.

PRESIDENT IKEDA: Diet plays an important part in many of these diseases in adults. Is the same true for children?

MORITA: Yes. In particular, snacking is a problem. Children who are constantly eating are going to be overweight. Snacks should only be given in small amounts and at times when they will not interfere with eating three solid meals a day.

TOYOFUKU: Lack of exercise is another cause of these problems. A survey in Japan on the amount of time that overweight children spent in physical activity after school showed that by far the majority had less than twenty minutes of activity a day.

PRESIDENT IKEDA: Yes, children today do not play outside the way they used to.

MORITA: Instead, they are inside playing computer games. The only part of their bodies that gets any exercise is their fingers!

TOYOFUKU: Yes, we often hear of children who are so physically unfit that they do not know how to put out their arms to break a fall, and as a result fall flat on their faces. Or children who cannot stand up straight, hard as they try, or are unable to dodge a ball thrown at them, so it hits them in the eye.

A Life of Convenience Obstructs Healthy Development

PRESIDENT IKEDA: Our convenient, modern lives seem to be hindering the healthy development of children. Children are a mirror that reflect the state of society. The comfortable modern lifestyle of children — who are driven in a car when they could walk, who are fed soft foods that are easy to chew, who live in rooms kept at an even temperature year round through heating and air-conditioning — is the creation of adults.

No child wants to become overweight or suffer from high blood pressure or diabetes. The family environment plays a major role in the formation of a child's habits. Adults can, to a certain degree, take care of their own health. Children cannot. Parents must protect the health of their children.

No child wants to become overweight or suffer from high blood pressure or diabetes. The family environment plays a major role in the formation of a child's habits. Adults can, to a certain degree, take care of their own health. Children cannot. Parents must protect the health of their children. It is important that parents have an awareness of their responsibility to work together with their children in creating a healthy life for them. Adults, therefore, need to examine and make changes where necessary, in their own lifestyles and habits.

In Japan, we live in an age where information, all kinds of convenient gadgets, and whatever food we desire are readily available. Precisely because it is such an age, parents must decide what is necessary and what is not to raise healthy children. It is an age that poses a challenge to the parents' wisdom and their lifestyles.

Sleep

Participants in this discussion on
' Humanism and the Art of Medicine:
A New Century of Health'
are SGI President Ikeda, Soka Gakkai
Doctors' Division Leaders Dr Shuhei Morita
and Dr Hiroyuki Toyofuku

PRESIDENT IKEDA: We are having one hot day after another. I am sure many people are having trouble sleeping. We spoke a little about this in our earlier discussion on 'Staying Healthy in the Summer'[1], but it bears repeating that sound sleep is very important in recovering from fatique and exhaustion brought on by the summer heat.

MORITA: Yes. Now that we are really entering into the hotter part of the year, I am sure that our readers appreciate this keenly.

TOYOFUKU: I am giving advice on this subject, and I certainly can!

PRESIDENT IKEDA: There is an old saying, "The beginning of health is sleep." Why is it that human beings need to sleep?

TOYOFUKU: The most important reason is that the brain needs to recuperate from fatique and mental exertion. Our muscles can recover from fatique through rest alone, without necessitating sleep. The brain, however, need sleep to recover.

PRESIDENT IKEDA: It is true that when you go without sufficient sleep for several days, or when you stay up all night, you feel unfocused and your brain does not function very well.

Sleep Increases Growth Hormone Production

TOYOFUKU: Yes. Experiments show that when sleep is interrupted, people can experience depression, irritability and emotional disturbances.

MORITA: Of course, sleep refreshes not only the brain but enables all parts of the body to recuperate from fatigue. There are hormones that are not produced in quantity unless we sleep. Growth hormone is one good example.

PRESIDENT IKEDA: I see. Perhaps that is where we get the Japanese saying, "A sleeping child grows up big and strong."

---

1. See pg 95-106.

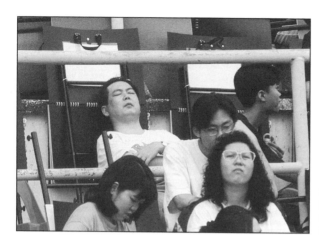

Sleep is life's 'chief nourisher', restoring vitality to tired minds and bodies.

MORITA: Sleep is also related to our immune system. The reason we advise someone who has caught a cold to get plenty of sleep is because sleep increases the body's ability to fight invading pathogens.

PRESIDENT IKEDA: Shakespeare had this to say of sleep:

> Sleep that knits up the ravell'd sleeve of care,
> The death of each day's life, sore labour's bath,
> Balm of hurt minds, great nature's second course,
> Chief nourisher in life's feast.[2]

Sleep certainly is life's 'chief nourisher', restoring vitality to tired minds and bodies.

How much sleep does a person need? Dr Linus Pauling (1901-1994) maintained that seven to nine hours of sleep is ideal.

Dr Pauling, recipient of two Nobel Prizes for chemistry and peace, respectively, is known as one of this century's most pre-eminent scientists. A dialogue between President Ikeda and Dr Pauling has been published under the title, A Lifelong Quest for Peace.

---

2. *Macbeth*, Act II, Scene ii, 1s. 37-40.

The Need for Sleep Changes with Age

MORITA: Japanese sleep an average of seven to eight hours. However, total sleep time changes with age. A newborn infant sleeps an average of eighteen hours a day; a ten-year-old child, about nine hours; and an adult, about eight. Then, as one ages, total sleep time increases again.

TOYOFUKU: The need for sleep varies greatly from one individual to the next. Some find eight hours sufficient, while others do not.

PRESIDENT IKEDA: That seems to be true even among those we regard as geniuses. It is said that Edison slept very little, while Einstein was a long sleeper.

MORITA: Feeling well rested and refreshed after sleep is not determined solely by the amount of time we sleep. The quality of our sleep is also very important.

REM and Non-REM Sleep

PRESIDENT IKEDA: That's true. Doctors often talk of the difference between REM sleep and non-REM sleep. REM sleep is light sleep, isn't it?

TOYOFUKU: Yes. REM stands for 'rapid eye movement'. The period of sleep when our eyes are moving rapidly is thought to be the phase when we are dreaming. In contrast, non-REM sleep is deep sleep. When we sleep, we passs through alternating periods of both kinds of sleep.

MORITA: A feeling of being refeshed by sleep, therefore, depends upon how much deep, non-REM sleep we have had.

TOYOFUKU: Of course, REM sleep serves a purpose as well. REM sleep is relatively light sleep for the brain, but it is the deepest sleep for the body. In that sense, we can say that REM sleep refreshes the body and non-REM sleep refeshes the mind.

PRESIDENT IKEDA: Speaking of dreaming during periods of REM sleep, a good dream can be really refreshing. The Lotus Sutra promises that those who practise the True Law will have wonderful dreams.[3]

The Buddhist scriptures describe some of the benefits of sound sleep as follows: (1) preventing insomnia; (2) pleasant waking; and (3) absence of bad dreams.[4]

Too Much Sleep also Causes Fatigue

PRESIDENT IKEDA: Is too much sleep bad for you? Dr Pauling asserted that less than seven hours and more than nine hours of sleep is not good for you.

MORITA: There have been experiments to determine the effects of too much sleep. They have shown that one loses the ability to concentrate and becomes less efficient at work. It is not true that the longer we sleep the more refreshed we feel. Sleeping too long can actually be fatiguing.

Those who are ill should get plenty of sleep, but even here too much sleep can sometimes upset the patient's biological rhythms. It is important for each of us to coordinate our sleep with our natural rhythm.

PRESIDENT IKEDA: Those who are ill should get plenty of sleep, but even here too much sleep can sometimes upset the patient's biological rhythms. It is important for each of us to coordinate our sleep with our natural rhythm.

The Great Teacher T'ien-tai of China warned against oversleeping, saying:

> With the fires of impermanence consuming the world, we cannot afford the leisure of slumber, if we are to quickly apprehend to the truth of birth and death.[5]

Buddhism expounds ten kinds of impediments to practise. Sleep is one of them. Of course, this does not mean that we should not get sufficient sleep.

---

3. In the 'Peaceful Practices' chapter of the Lotus Sutra, it states: "Anyone who reads this sutra . . . / even in his dreams / he will see only wonderful things." (LS14, 209-210)
4. Contained in *Juju Ritsu* (The Ten Division of Monastic Rules). The *vinaya* or rules of discipline of the Sarvastivada school, translated from Sanskrit into Chinese by Punyatara and Kumarajiva.
5. From *Sho-shikan* (Abridged 'Concentration and Insight'), an abridgement of the *Maka Shikan* (Great Concentration and Insight) made by T'ien-t'ai.

What it means is that a lazy and sluggish attitude towards life produces nothing of enduring value. A life without self-disciplined effort towards personal improvement and development, a life of simply drifting with the flow, is empty and meaningless.

The determination to devote all of one's energies to creating something, to leaving behind some legacy of achievement for the future is the foundation on which a healthy mental and physical life is built. Nichiren Daishonin cautions, "You must not spend your lives in vain and regret it for ten thousand years to come." (WND, pg 622) Leonardo da Vinci wrote, "As a well-spent day brings happy sleep, so life well used brings happy death."[6]

Making each day fulfilling is important. A fulfilled life is an eternal treasure.

Fighting Insomnia

TOYOFUKU: Everyone wishes to sleep peacefully. But this can be difficult for some.

PRESIDENT IKEDA: Yes. The Swiss philosopher, Carl Hilty (1833-1909), said, "Sleepless nights are an affliction hard to endure, and they are feared by the well and the sick alike."[7]

In Hilty's case, though, an abiding interest in the subject of insomnia led him to write a book, called *For Sleepless Nights* . . .

MORITA: As far as treating insomnia is concerned, when sleeplessness continues for only two or three days, stress is usually the cause, and it generally cures itself. But if insomnia should persist for more than a month, it could be an indicator of an undetected illness, and one should consult a doctor. Insomnia can also be caused by psychosomatic illness, neurosis or depression.

PRESIDENT IKEDA: What are some of the points we should bear in mind if we want to get a good night's sleep?

---

6. *The Notebooks of Leonardo da Vinci*, trans Edward MacCurdy (New York: George Braziller, 1958), volume I, pg 67.
7. Translated from German: Carl Hilty, *Fur Schlaflose Nachte* (For Sleepless Nights) (Leipzig: J.C. Hinrichs'sche Buchhandelung, 1908), pg 1.

TOYOFUKU: The first thing is to establish and maintain a regular daily rhythm. Even if you cannot sleep, try to go to bed at the same time every night and to get up at the same time every morning.

PRESIDENT IKEDA: Many people try to make up for lack of sleep on workdays by sleeping in over the weekend, hoping to build up a store of sleep to get them through the coming week.

TOYOFUKU: I am afraid that only disrupts their regular sleep rhythm.

PRESIDENT IKEDA: They are probably the very ones who are always late coming to work on Monday mornings!

TOYOFUKU: We should make an effort to get up at the usual time even on holidays. We can always take an afternoon nap if we feel we need to get some extra sleep. The main thing is not to disrupt our normal daily sleep schedule.

PRESIDENT IKEDA: It is important to maintain a regular rhythm to our lives. Mr Toda said we should try to get to bed by midnight. We would feel far more refreshed in the morning if we did so, he asserted, than if we went to bed after midnight.

Sleep is an activity where we fuse our lives with the universe and recharge ourselves with that vast life force. That is why it is important to stay in tune with the rhythm of life and the universe.

MORITA: Sitting in the sun or taking a walk in the morning can be effective in curing insomnia. Sunlight helps us adjust our body rhythm. These methods are especially useful for the elderly.

PRESIDENT IKEDA: Why is it that it is harder to sleep as one grows older?

TOYOFUKU: Sleep is controlled by the brain, and as our brain deteriorates with age, our ability to maintain the sleep rhythm of our younger years is reduced.

MORITA: In particular, it takes longer for older people to fall asleep. Their sleep is also generally shallower, which is why they may not feel as refreshed or satisfied by their sleep as they were when they were younger.

PRESIDENT IKEDA: The custom of the siesta, an afternoon nap, survives in Southern Europe and Central and South America. What does a nap do for us?

TOYOFUKU: Generally, if an afternoon nap is less than an hour long, it can be helpful in curing insomnia during the night. Of course, I am not encouraging people to nod off at their desks during work . . .

MORITA: Long naps, however, and naps too late in the afternoon can prevent one from being sleepy when bedtime comes and getting a good night's rest.

Too Much Alcohol Obstructs Sleep

PRESIDENT IKEDA: Is there anything we can do before going to bed to help us sleep soundly?

MORITA: Before going to bed, try to relax as much as possible. Avoid vigorous activity or television programmes that are too stimulating.

PRESIDENT IKEDA: Do you recommend taking a bath before going to sleep?

TOYOFUKU: A lukewarm bath can be helpful in promoting sleep.
But a hot bath aften overstimulates the body and can end up keeping one awake.

MORITA: Those who feel the cold easily or suffer from chills should wear socks to bed or sleep with a hot-water bottle to warm themselves.

TOYOFUKU: One should also avoid drinking large quantities of caffeine-containing beverages, such as coffee, black tea or green tea. Drinking a cup of warm milk before bedtime can be helpful in getting a restful night. Eating a small portion of dairy product, such as cheese or yogurt, can also help some people sleep.

PRESIDENT IKEDA: Some say that they cannot fall asleep without the aid of alcohol. Though in some cases one may suspect this is just an excuse to have a drink . . .

MORITA: A small portion of alcohol can relax one and help one sleep, but too much will make one's throat dry or act as a diuretic, forcing one to get up several times in the night to use the bathroom. If we want to get a good night's sleep, I think we should keep our consumption of alcohol to a minimum.

Eat a Good Lunch on Hot Days

PRESIDENT IKEDA: Getting into bed and focusing all your energy on going to sleep can end up just making you tense and keeping you awake.

TOYOFUKU: Yes, it is easier to fall asleep if you do not spend too much time worrying about trying to do so. To take your mind off it, it is a good idea to play some soft, soothing music or listen to the radio.

PRESIDENT IKEDA: What about the pillow we use?

TOYOFUKU: A pillow should be the right height to support the natural curve of the bones from the neck to the head. Lower pillows tend to be better than high ones.

PRESIDENT IKEDA: I think it was Benjamin Franklin who said, "Weariness is the best pillow."
What about the mattress we sleep on?

MORITA: A mattress should be on the firm side, supporting the body's natural posture and making it easy to turn over and move about. The important thing is to choose the mattress on which you can sleep most comfortably.

PRESIDENT IKEDA: Have you any hints for sleeping soundly in the sweltering weather we are experiencing in Japan right now?

TOYOFUKU: Resting your head on a cold-water pillow or sleeping on a reed mat spread on top of the sheets of your bed or futon can make for a pleasant night's sleep by cooling you and allowing your perspiration to evaporate efficiently.

MORITA: In summer, it is best to eat a good, solid lunch, and then a light supper. A high-calorie meal in the evening raises your body temperature and can obstruct sleep.

Talk to Your Doctor before Taking any Sleeping Medication

PRESIDENT IKEDA: Is it all right to take sleeping tablets? I am sure many are afraid they might become addicted to such medication.

> **The real secret to healthy sleep is what we do during the day. Has that day been a satisfying and fulfilling one, mentally and physically? In turn, a night's healthy sleep contributes to our healthy activity the following day.**

MORITA: The kinds of sleeping pills that doctors prescribe today are generally very safe and not very addictive.

TOYOFUKU: But one must take them as prescribed. Always talk to your doctor to make sure you are taking the medicine best suited to you. And, never take more than the prescribed dosage.

PRESIDENT IKEDA: We must not play doctor ourselves, right?

MORITA: Yes. And when stopping a course of sleeping medication, it is important that you do not stop all at once. Follow your doctor's instructions and reduce the dosage a little bit at a time.

You should also never drink alcohol before or after taking medication.

TOYOFUKU: Sleeping pills exhibit increased potency in the elderly, so I recommend them to avoid taking such medication.

PRESIDENT IKEDA: We should not think of sleeping pills as a cure for insomnia, but merely as an aid towards solving the problem. Sleep appears to be a world of stillness and repose. But life itself never rests; it is continually active. We cannot expect to be able to sleep soundly without realising the importance sleep has to our life as a whole. The real secret to healthy sleep is what we do during the day. Has that day been a satisfying and fulfilling one, mentally and physically? In turn, a night's healthy sleep contributes to our healthy activity the following day. As someone once said: "Sleep is the golden chain that ties health and our bodies together.[8]

I hope that all of our readers will create day after day of golden value, with the help of night after night of sound and refreshing sleep.

---

8. Thomas Dekker, *The Gull's Hornbook, ii, (1609)*.

Atopic Eczema

Participants in this discussion on
' Humanism and the Art of Medicine:
A New Century of Health'
are SGI President Ikeda, Soka Gakkai
Doctors' Division Leaders Dr Shuhei Morita
and Dr Hiroyuki Toyofuku

MORITA: We had a tremendous response to our earlier instalment on children's health — no doubt because so many children are on summer vacation right now. Quite a few people wrote to us, asking if we would talk about atopic eczema[1], a chronic skin disorder that seems to be afflicting an increasing number of children in Japan in recent years.

PRESIDENT IKEDA: Is that so? This seems to indicate that this form of eczema is quite prevalent.

TOYOFUKU: According to a survey by the Ministry of Health and Welfare, one out of three Japanese children of age three were diagnosed with atopic eczema.

PRESIDENT IKEDA: I believe it is on the increase in adults as well, isn't it?

MORITA: Yes. Symptoms usually begin to appear in children from the age of about six months, and in most cases the condition clears up around adolescence. Recently, however, there has been a marked increase in cases where the atopic eczema has persisted into adulthood or manifests for the first time then.

PRESIDENT IKEDA: The word *atopic* is derived from Greek for 'unusual' or 'uncommon', isn't it?

TOYOFUKU: Yes. *Atopic* came into usage to describe a hereditary hypersensitivity that predisposes certain people to allergic diseases, such as asthma, rhinitis, conjunctivitis and pollinosis. It was chosen to denote the 'unusual' nature of this idiosyncratic genetic constitution, the cause of which is unknown.

MORITA: But atopic eczema is not simply a matter of a genetic predisposition. That said, however, we still do not fully understand what causes the disorder or how it develops.

PRESIDENT IKEDA: I guess, then, it still remains an 'unusual' illness. Are there

---

1. Atopic eczema: Also known as atopic dermatitis. A skin condition characterised by red, scaly patches, usually on the face, neck, hands, feet, in the crook of the elbow or behind the knees. It is accompanied by extreme dryness of the skin, the cause of intense itching.

a number of different theories as to what might be its causes?

TOYOFUKU: Yes. But the most commonly suspected causes are: (1) living environment, (2) diet, or (3) stress.

A Vicious Cycle of Itching and Scratching

PRESIDENT IKEDA: I see. Let us discuss those causes in detail later.

What about the symptoms? I understand that the primary symptom of atopic eczema is terrible itching.

No matter how much one scratches, the itching persists, and the patient scratches so hard that the skin is broken. When a sore of that kind develops, it becomes susceptible to bacterial invasion, which only aggravates the itching and the overall condition.

MORITA: That is right. Regardless of the age of the sufferer, a rash appears on the skin, and it is extremely itchy. It can be so irritating that it prevents sleep at night.

TOYOFUKU: No matter how much one scratches, the itching persists, and the patient scratches so hard that the skin is broken. When a sore of that kind develops, it becomes susceptible to bacterial invasion, which only aggravates the itching and the overall condition.

PRESIDENT IKEDA: It is a vicious cycle, isn't it?

MORITA: Yes. People who are affected with atopic eczema usually have dry skin to begin with. Since the skin lacks moisture, there are small openings between the cells, creating an opportunity for bacteria and their toxic by-products to enter the skin.

TOYOFUKU: Any itching is a reaction of the nerves beneath the skin to irritation. In the case of atopic eczema, the nerves are especially sensitised.

PRESIDENT IKEDA: In other words, the patient has an enhanced sensitivity to itching.

MORITA: Yes. That is why one of the basic treatments for it is very careful skin care, so that bacteria cannot invade the skin.

Follow the Doctor's Directions in Applying Ointments

PRESIDENT IKEDA: What kind of skin care is specifically recommended for sufferers of atopic eczema?

MORITA: Soaking in a warm bath is said to be good. It is more effective when two baths of this kind are taken a day — one in the morning and one in the evening. Very hot baths, however, are to be avoided because they only tend to increase the itching.

TOYOFUKU: Bathing washes away the bacteria on the skin's surface. After the bath, one should apply a moisturising cream or lotion to restore and preserve the skin's moisture.

PRESIDENT IKEDA: Is it all right to use soap and shampoo?

MORITA: One can use them, but one should not rub or scrub the skin too hard because it will remove all the vital natural oils. It is also important to thoroughly rinse away soap or shampoo. The perfumes contained in many such products can irritate the skin.

TOYOFUKU: It is also important that washing agents be thoroughly rinsed from the clothing when it is washed. Cotton, meanwhile, is the preferred fabric for any garments that come in direct contact with the skin, such as underwear and socks. It causes the least irritation.

PRESIDENT IKEDA: Are there any effective ointments for atopic eczema?

MORITA: When the skin is really irritated, the doctor may prescribe a steroid lotion or cream to apply.

TOYOFUKU: Different steroid creams are used for different parts of the body, so one should always check with the doctor for the appropriate ointment. It is important to follow the doctor's directions closely. If you just apply it wherever you think or stop using it when you feel like it, there may be side-effects.

It is important that washing agents be thoroughly rinsed from the clothing when it is washed.

Taking Special Care to Air and Vacuum Bedding

PRESIDENT IKEDA: If the rash does not clear up in spite of the skin care methods we have discussed, I guess it is time to turn to the other three factors: living environment, diet and stress. Let us start with living environment.

TOYOFUKU: All right. Dust mites are a great aggravator of atopic eczema.

PRESIDENT IKEDA: Dust mites?

MORITA: Yes. Dust mites prefer warm, humid environments. Since the introduction of modern glass windows enclosed in aluminum sashes, Japanese homes today have much poorer air circulation than they did in former times when they were constructed of wood. In addition, the growing popularity of central heating means that we keep our homes warm all winter long.

PRESIDENT IKEDA: I guess that not only makes a pleasant environment for people, but also for the dust mites!

TOYOFUKU: Yes, indeed. We cannot see them, but they are living with us all the time.

PRESIDENT IKEDA: What can we do about them?

MORITA: Well, the main thing is to try to restrict their numbers by reducing the places where they can reside. Among practical measures we can take are airing our bedding thoroughly on a regular basis, not neglecting to beat our futon, quilts and covers outdoors to remove dust and debris. We can also vacuum our mattress or futon to remove the dust mites that might have made their home in it.

Toyofuku: It is best to avoid having carpets and rugs in the home as well. But if you have them, vacuum both the surface and the underside, where possible.

President Ikeda: It is important to be thorough.

Toyofuku: That is correct. Dust and moulds are irritants, too, so clean very carefully and thoroughly. It is also important to wash or vacuum curtains regularly and to clean behind and under furniture — keeping everything spick-and-span from top to bottom. Having stuffed toys and cushions in the house should probably be avoided as well because they accumulate dust and provide a place for dust mites to dwell. Keeping pets inside is also not advisable where a family member suffers from atopic eczema.

Morita: Keeping the windows closed all the time makes it humid and stuffy inside the house, so a conscious effort should be made to open the windows from time to time to let in fresh air.

President Ikeda: You also mentioned that diet could aggravate atopic eczema.

Toyofuku: Yes. Children are often allergic to certain foods, such as eggs, soyabean products or milk, and that can worsen their eczema. But simply avoiding these foods can lead to an unbalanced diet that can adversely affect their growth.

Morita: I think it is best for parents to consult with a doctor or dietician about the diet appropriate for a child suffering from this disorder.

Allergies are Overreactions of the Immune System

President Ikeda: The increase in atopic eczema in Japan in recent years can be attributed to changes in our housing and living environment and in our

diet. In that sense, I suppose we can say that it is a modern disease.
Could we call atopic eczema a kind of allergy?

TOYOFUKU: It is an allergic disorder, yes.

PRESIDENT IKEDA: The word *allergy* also derives from Greek. If I remember correctly, it means 'different reaction', doesn't it?

MORITA: Yes.

PRESIDENT IKEDA: What and how is an allergy a 'different reaction'?

MORITA: All people have an immune system which serves to neutralise and eliminate viruses and bacteria that invade the body. But sometimes the body's defence mechanism can overreact and inflict harm on the body rather than protecting it. This 'different reaction' is what we call an allergy.

PRESIDENT IKEDA: A rash that appears when a person eats, for example, mackerel or eggs is an allergic response, then?

MORITA: Yes, because the body is reacting to something that normally would not produce such a response in the average person.

PRESIDENT IKEDA: You might say it is a case of one man's food being another man's poison.

TOYOFUKU: That is precisely the situation with food allergies. What causes allergies differs greatly from one person to another.

Encourage Rather than Scold

PRESIDENT IKEDA: Stress can also be a cause of atopic eczema, can't it?

TOYOFUKU: Yes. Continued stress can aggravate atopic eczema. For example, it has been found that Japanese junior and senior high school students who suffer from this disorder tend to experience a worsening of the condition during the high-pressure period of studying and taking entrance examinations for the next stage of their schooling, only to recover when the examinations are over and the outcome decided.

MORITA: Another major source of stress is the actual activity of scratching the itching that accompanies atopic eczema. It feels good while one's scratching, but afterwards the condition is only made worse. This leads to self-recrimination and depression on the part of the sufferer, who knows all too well the negative effects of scratching.

> **There is a saying that the skin is the mirror of the mind. Our skin is very delicate and sensitive to our moods.**

PRESIDENT IKEDA: I am sure it is also very stressful for parents to see their children scratching the rash, when they have warned them time and again that it will only make it worse.

TOYOFUKU: Yes. And, when they scold the child — "What! You are scratching again?" — it only adds to the child's stress.

PRESIDENT IKEDA: Another vicious circle. Eventually, the whole family becomes edgy and tense. The important thing to remember is that scolding does not solve anything. It is much better for parents to encourage the child, saying, "We'll gradually cure this — you will see," or "This will all clear up when you get a little older," as they gently apply the proper ointment.

A King Who Suffered a Stress-induced Skin Disease

PRESIDENT IKEDA: There is a saying that the skin is the mirror of the mind. Our skin is very delicate and sensitive to our moods. During Sakyamuni's lifetime, King Ajatasatru, the famous ruler of Magadha, suffered from a terrible skin disease, his body covered with purulent boils.[2] His mother applied various salves and ointments, but to no avail. His condition only grew worse. Finally, the king told her that it was not a disease of the body but of the spirit, and he expressed doubts whether anyone could cure it. In the broadest

---

2. This episode appears in the Gosho, *On Curing Karmic Disease*, (WND, pg 632 [MW-II-214-215 [249]).

sense, I think we could say that the cause of King Ajatasatru's illness was severe stress.

While still crown prince, Ajatasatru had become friends with the evil Devadatta, at whose instigation he harshly oppressed Sakyamuni and his followers. Under Devadatta's influence, Ajatasatru also usurped the throne from his father, King Bimbisara, whom he imprisoned and drove to his death. His father's demise filled Ajatasatru with great remorse, and his distress at his past actions manifested itself as this terrible skin disease.

In the Nirvana Sutra it states that, seeing Ajatasatru's suffering, Sakyamuni went into a state known as the 'moon-loving' meditation[3]. While in meditation, a brilliant ray of light of clear coolness issued from the Buddha's body and fell upon Ajatasatru, whereupon the festering boils that covered him here instantly healed.

By meeting again with Sakyamuni, Ajatasatru was able to cure the disease of the spirit that was the cause of his boils. From that time on, the Magadhan king vowed to dedicate himself to spreading Sakyamuni's teachings, and he enjoyed good health in both body and mind ever after.

MORITA: I think it is important to have the strength of mind and inner fortitude not to be defeated by stress. The encouragement of those around us is also very important.

Since there is no definitive cure for atopic eczema, it is quite possible that stress incurred as a result of suffering from this painful skin disorder can make the condition worse.

TOYOFUKU: It is certainly true that there is no 'guaranteed cure' for this condition. The symptoms and causes of atopic eczema are complex and diverse, and the method of treatment will therefore be different for each patient.

MORITA: I do not mean to completely reject home remedies, but it can be dangerous to try all sorts of different treatments. I have heard of several quack remedies being marketed. All they are good for is bilking you of your hard-earned money. It may take time, but the best approach is to work as a team with a doctor in whom you feel confident, and search patiently for

---

3. Moon-loving meditation: Here the boundless compassion of the Buddha is compared to the moonlight which releases one from uneasiness and brings peace of mind.

the method of treatment that works best for the patient.

PRESIDENT IKEDA: Giving in to feelings of frustration and impatience can be dangerous. It can blind you so you can no longer see things as they really are. Anxiety and worry will not make the patient's condition any better. If anything, it will only aggravate it.

I hope that both sufferers of atopic eczema and their families will patiently continue the proper treatment with the shared determination to conquer the disease over time.

Gastrointestinal Disorders

Participants in this discussion on
' Humanism and the Art of Medicine:
A New Century of Health'
are SGI President Ikeda, Soka Gakkai
Doctors' Division Leaders Dr Shuhei Morita,
Dr Hiroyuki Toyofuku, and a special guest,
Vice-Secretary Yoichi Uehigashi

PRESIDENT IKEDA: Today, we will be talking about gastrointestinal disorders from which so many people suffer. Such ailments are also known to be strongly influenced by our mental state. Dr Uehigashi is an expert in this area of medicine, so we have invited him to join our discussion today for the benefit of our readers.

UEHIGASHI: I am very glad to have the chance to participate in a discussion of this particular subject.

Summer is a season when, because of the heat, many people are afflicted with stomach problems.

PRESIDENT IKEDA: Among the major causes of stomach problems around this time of the year, I guess, are excessive consumption of cold liquids, over-exposure to air-conditioning and catching a chill while sleeping. Am I right?

UEHIGASHI: Yes. There is also evidence that the gastrointestinal tract does not function as well in hot weather.

MORITA: So, the folk wisdom that it is better to eat easily digestible foods in summer is indeed valid. Of course, we still have to be careful to maintain a well-balanced diet.

PRESIDENT IKEDA: What kind of ailments do such frequently reported symptoms as stomach pain, indigestion or a heavy feeling in the stomach point to?

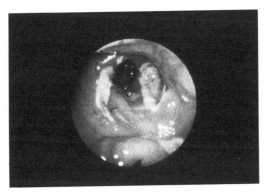

Double ('kissing') duodenal ulcer.

UEHIGASHI: They usually point to stress or fatigue. Occasionally, they may be signs of gastritis (an inflammation of the stomach lining), or of a gastric or duodenal ulcer.

PRESIDENT IKEDA: What is the difference between gastritis and an ulcer?

UEHIGASHI: To put it simply, gastritis is an inflammation in the stomach. The lining of the stomach is inflamed or slightly eroded. An ulcer, meanwhile, is a deep perforation in the stomach lining.

PRESIDENT IKEDA: Is gastritis the most common stomach ailment?

TOYOFUKU: Yes. There are two kinds of gastritis, acute and chronic.

PRESIDENT IKEDA: How are they different?

UEHIGASHI: Acute gastritis is usually caused by irritants, such as aspirin and similar pain relievers, or sudden, intense stress. On the other hand, chronic gastritis which we have recently discovered is usually caused by a bacteria known as *H pylori*[1] bacteria that lives between the stomach lining and the layer of mucus that protects it. There are, unfortunately, no easily recognisable symptoms to indicate the presence of chronic gastritis.

PRESIDENT IKEDA: What are the symptoms of ulcers?

UEHIGASHI: Some people feel pain in the pit of their stomach when the stomach is empty, with the pain diminishing after a meal has been eaten. Others experience pain when the stomach is full.

MORITA: In extreme cases, the patient may vomit blood or pass stools that have the shiny, black appearance of coal tar.

PRESIDENT IKEDA: Because of the high incidence of stomach cancer in Japan, I am sure many Japanese worry they might have cancer when they experience stomach pain.

---

1. Also known in full as *Helicobacter pylori*.

UEHIGASHI: In the majority of cases, a medical examination will show that stomach pain is the result of mild gastritis or an ulcer, not cancer.

TOYOFUKU: While I do not want to get into a detailed discussion of cancer in this instalment — perhaps we can save it for a later one — I would like to point out that stomach cancer is completely different from gastritis or ulcers. In stomach cancer, the cells of the stomach lining change into cancer cells and reproduce at an extraordinary rate.

UEHIGASHI: It is worth noting, however, that in most cases, there are no obvious symptoms in the earliest stages of stomach cancer — and, if there are symptoms, they may be similar to those of gastritis or ulcers.

PRESIDENT IKEDA: Amateur diagnosis is dangerous, then, isn't it?

MORITA: Regular medical check-ups by a qualified physician are highly recommended.

Heart Disease can Cause Pain in the Upper Abdomen

PRESIDENT IKEDA: Are there cases in which the abdominal or stomach area hurts in spite of the fact that it is not directly experiencing any physical disorder?

UEHIGASHI: Yes. Diseases of the digestive system, such as gallstones or pancreatitis (an inflammation of the pancreas), can cause sharp pain in the abdomen, as can heart disorders, such as angina or cardiac arrest.

PRESIDENT IKEDA: So, abdominal pain can be a sign of some illness completely unrelated to the stomach? That is a little frightening.

UEHIGASHI: Yes. People often blame their stomach for illnesses that actually have nothing to do with that organ.

MORITA: The innocent stomach condemned without a trail!

TOYOFUKU: What all of these show is that the stomach is a very sensitive indicator of our mental and physical state.

Our feelings and emotions have a direct effect on the stomach, and "The stomach is the mirror of the heart," and "The stomach is the resonance chamber of the emotions."

PRESIDENT IKEDA: Yes, our feelings and emotions have a direct effect on the stomach, do not they? I have heard it said, "The stomach is the mirror of the heart," and "The stomach is the resonance chamber of the emotions."

In Japanese, as it also appears to be the case in many other languages, the word *stomach* (*hara*) often appears in expressions used to convey one's mind or intention, or emotional states, such as anger or impatience.

MORITA: There is an expression, too, *haraguroi* (literary, 'black-stomached') which means 'wicked', 'scheming' or 'black-hearted'.

TOYOFUKU: And then, there is the ever popular *hara ga tatsu* (literary, 'my stomach stands up'), which means 'to be angry, outraged or annoyed'.

PRESIDENT IKEDA: Actually, I think *tatsu* ('stands up') in that expression means 'begins to move'. When you grow angry, your stomach often begins to churn.

Is it true, Dr Uehigashi, that anger and frustration have a strong effect on the stomach?

Digestion is Impeded by Anger and Anxiety

UEHIGASHI: Yes, indeed. They have a very strong and immediate effect. Anger, fear and anxiety impede digestion.

Under normal circumstances when the stomach becomes active in the digestive process, the blood vessels along the walls of the gastrointestinal tract expand to allow for increased blood flow. But severe emotional upsets or intense stress disrupt the operation of the autonomic nervous system and its ability to regulate the digestive processes correctly. There is a sharp drop in the blood supply to the stomach, along with the vital oxygen and nutrition it normally delivers.

PRESIDENT IKEDA: When this process is repeated frequently enough, it can lead to ulcers, can't it?

UEHIGASHI: In the most simple terms, an ulcer could be described as a condition where the gastric juice — normally secreted by the stomach for the digestion of food — has digested the stomach lining instead.

TOYOFUKU: Just picturing it is enough to make one wince!

UEHIGASHI: The gastric juice is so highly acidic that, if you were to place a few drops in the palm of your hand, it would create a blister on your skin. It is precisely because of this high acidity that it can digest most foods. The fascinating thing about the stomach is that, under normal circumstances, it does not digest the stomach itself.

MORITA: I am reminded of an old short story about a scientist who invented a medicine that could dissolve anything, but all came to naught because he could not find any container to place it in.

The Stomach's Balance of Defence and Attack

UEHIGASHI: The stomach is lined with a layer of mucus, which functions as a kind of 'wall of defence'. In a healthy stomach, an equilibrium is maintained between the 'attack' of the gastric juice and the 'defence' of the protective mucous layer.

PRESIDENT IKEDA: This is a wonderful example of the mystic function of life. The microcosm of the human body operates according to wondrous processes.

Speaking of attack and defence, I am reminded of the origin of the Japanese word for 'contradiction' (*mujun*) [which derives from the Chinese word (*maodun*) and is written with the same Chinese characters].

Long ago, in the Chu kingdom of ancient China, there was a fellow selling lances (*mu*) and shields (*jun*). He bragged that his lances would pierce any shield and his shields withstand any lance. Then a prospective customer asked him what would happen if he struck one of his own shields with one of his own lances. This is the origin of the Japanese word for 'contradiction', meaning two propositions that invalidate each other.

In the case of our stomach, the gastric juice is the lance and the mucus is the shield. Normally, the shield is stronger; when the lance is stronger and pierces through the shield, an ulcer develops.

UEHIGASHI: Precisely. The increased strength of the lance means too much gastric juice is being secreted (excess stomach acid). The weakening of the shield means a decreased production of protective mucus. When the blood flow to the stomach is reduced, the protective mucous shield is weakened, and the lance pierces through those portions that have been particularly weakened, causing the formation of an ulcer.

A Sharp Increase in Ulcers after the Kobe-Osaka Earthquake

MORITA: The autonomic nervous system plays an important role in the normal operation of the gastrointestinal system. But stress can easily upset the natural balance.

TOYOFUKU: Surveys show that in the two months after the devastating Kobe-Osaka Earthquake, people who had been affected by the disaster exhibited a sharp increase of ulcer symptoms, including vomiting blood. It appears that the fear and anxiety triggered by the earthquake caused great stress among survivors, leading to many developing ulcers as a result.

MORITA: On the other hand, there are also cases in which warm words of support and encouragement can actually improve the symptoms of illness and disease. We often see patients who come for an examination because they are worried about cancer. The doctor's reassurance after the check-up that it is nothing more than, say, gastritis, can cause their worries to evaporate and even the symptoms they had been suffering from to disappear.

UEHIGASHI: Experiments have also shown that when a completely healthy person is told there is something wrong with their stomach, the amount of gastric juice secreted suddenly doubles.

PRESIDENT IKEDA: It seems that it is important not to let stress get the better of you. Yet, though it is important to reduce stress, we can never escape it completely as long as we live. The secret is to confront stress and deal with it successfully.

Stress is like a ferocious dog. If you run away from it in fear, it will come after you. The same is true if you try to escape from your worries: They will only pursue you ever more fiercely. On the other hand, if you calmly and bravely face your anxieties head on, you will not only avoid unnecessary stress but grow stronger. You will become healthier, too.

TOYOFUKU: Positive thinking can actually turn stress to one's advantage.

The Role of *H pylori*

PRESIDENT IKEDA: Are there any other factors besides stress that can upset the stomach's balance between defence and attack?

UEHIGASHI: Yes, the *H pylori* that we discussed earlier. This particular bacteria has been found to be closely linked to gastritis, ulcers and other gastric disorders.

PRESIDENT IKEDA: Do you mean this bacteria is impervious to stomach acid?

UEHIGASHI: *H pylori* possesses an enzyme that can produce ammonia, which is highly alkaline, from urea, which is produced from the breakdown of protein in the digestive process. It survives in the stomach by using that enzyme to neutralise the stomach acid in its immediate environment.

TOYOFUKU: The ammonia produced by *H pylori* is also said to affect the mucous layer of the stomach, weakening its protective power.

PRESIDENT IKEDA: What should we do to keep our stomach operating in top condition?

UEHIGASHI: First, as far as dietary habits are concerned, eat regular meals, chew food thoroughly, eat a well-balanced diet and don't overeat — leave some room in your stomach at the end of every meal.

TOYOFUKU: Skipping breakfast or eating very late at night destroy the natural rhythm of digestion, absorption and elimination.

PRESIDENT IKEDA: In Japan, the traditional panacea for an upset stomach has been to eat plain rice gruel with a pickled plum in it.

UEHIGASHI: That is not a bad idea. When the stomach is not functioning well, rice gruel is a good food. But it is important, as it is with regular cooked rice, to chew it thoroughly.

PRESIDENT IKEDA: Chewing food thoroughly is really important, is not it?

UEHIGASHI: It certainly is. When food is chewed into small particles and mixed with saliva, the digestive enzymes in the saliva can effectively do their job of preparing the food for digestion, thus lightening the load on the stomach. It is also a fact that if we take time to chew our food properly, we are likely to feel satisfied before our stomach becomes completely full.

PRESIDENT IKEDA: I am sure that people of different ages and in different states of health should be concerned with different things.

MORITA: Yes. Older people produce less stomach acid and less saliva. The stomach's digestive capacity begins to decline. As a result, they should eat more lightly flavoured foods, and prepare food in a way that 'softens' it, such as boiling or steaming.

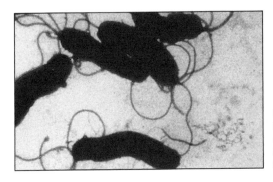

H. pylori, *a pathogen with a worldwide distribution, causes chronic gastritis, and is a major factor in the aetiology of peptic ulcer disease.*

UEHIGASHI: The method of preparation has a large effect on a food's digestibility. For example, a soft-boiled egg is said to be easier to digest than a hard-boiled egg.

TOYOFUKU: With the exception of those suffering from severe stomach problems or who have been instructed otherwise by their physician, it is important to eat adequate amounts of protein, the sources of which include eggs, milk, meat and fish.

UEHIGASHI: It is also wise to avoid smoking, highly spiced foods and too much alcohol. Too much coffee is also not recommended.

MORITA: On the other hand, if you are always worrying about what you should and should not eat and drink, you will only end up stressed, which is no good, either!

PRESIDENT IKEDA: It is important to eat meals in a pleasant and leisurely fashion. Busy as our lives may be, I think there are many surprisingly simple ways in which we can arrange this.

Stress as a Source of Growth

PRESIDENT IKEDA: It seems that many people who have stomach problems, though not severe enough to warrant a trip to the doctor, use over-the-counter remedies of different kinds to aid digestion.

UEHIGASHI: I do not think such remedies are a problem as a temporary measure. But it is important to remember that persistent symptoms, even if not severe, should be looked at by a doctor, in order to get to the root of the trouble.

PRESIDENT IKEDA: The Japanese writer, Natsume Soseki (1867-1916), also suffered from stomach problems. In his novel, *I am a Cat* (1905), he depicts Dr Kushami — the owner of the cat — trying all sorts of home-made remedies for his irritable stomach. Since the time that novel was written, a wide variety of effective stomach medicines have been developed.

But the secret to good digestion is to adopt a healthy lifestyle and to deal with the problem of stress in a constructive manner.

TOYOFUKU: That is right. We need to take steps to arrange our lives so that we have the proper balance of work and relaxation.

PRESIDENT IKEDA: Once I was engaged in a discussion with the French-born American microbiologist, Dr Renê Dubois (1901-1982), of the Rockefeller Institute for Medical Research in New York City [in November 1973]. In one of his books, he wrote:

> While it may be comforting to imagine a life free of stresses and strains in a carefree world, this will remain in idle dream . . . Man has elected to fight, not necessarily for himself, but for a process of emotional, intellectual, and ethical growth that goes on forever. To grow in the midst of dangers is the fate of the human race, because it is the law of the spirit.[2]

Life is a continuous struggle, so let us enjoy the challenge! Resolving to do so is ultimately the key to a healthy stomach.

I have heard it said that the intestinal tracts of modern humans are weaker than those of their ancestors. Is this true?

MORITA: Some have suggested that the reason so many people have been

---

2. René Dubos, *Mirage of Health: Utopias, Progress, and Biological Change* (New York: Doubleday & Company, Inc, 1959), pg 230.

affected by the toxin-producing bacteria, *E. coli 0157*[3], in Japan this summer is partly a result of weakened intestinal tracts.

UEHIGASHI: I don't know if the two are related, but it certainly is true that our intestinal tracts are weaker than they once were.

PRESIDENT IKEDA: The function of our intestinal tract is to absorb nutrients into the body, so if it is weakened, we won't have the energy that we should. Why has this weakening happened?

UEHIGASHI: It is thought to be influenced by stress and processed foods, which are high in additives.

PRESIDENT IKEDA: In what way specifically?

UEHIGASHI: The intestinal tract is the home of some one hundred varieties of bacteria — over one hundred trillion[4] individual organisms. They can be divided into 'the good guys' and 'the bad guys'.

TOYOFUKU: Just like human society!

Fibre Increases the Number of 'Good Bacteria'

UEHIGASHI: The good bacteria assist in the absorption of nutrients and protect the intestinal tract from toxins and disease — causing bacteria. They also produce beneficial substances, such as vitamin K. The bad bacteria cause food in the intestines to putrefy and produces various toxins.

Lactobacillus bifidus and other species of lactobacilli are typical beneficial bacteria, while Clostridium perfringen *(also known as Welch's bacillus and can be a cause of* enteritis *or* appendicitis *under certain conditions) is a typical pathogenic bacteria.*

---

3. *E. coli 0157*: Full name *Escherichia coli 0157*: H7. Causes haemorrhagic diarrhoea and in serious cases can lead to death. A brief discussion of this bacteria in connection to food poisoning appeared earlier in this series. (See — 'Staying Healthy in Summer', pg 95-106.)
4. One hundred trillion: 10^{14}.

The bad bacteria relish meat. They also proliferate when stress is present. Today, we experience much more stress in our lives and eat more meat than our ancestors did. This has led to an increase in the bad bacteria in our intestinal tract and, hence, to its gradual weakening.

PRESIDENT IKEDA: I see. Is there any way to reduce the amount of harmful bacteria?

UEHIGASHI: The total population of all bacteria in the intestinal tract remains largely constant, so the best method for decreasing the numbers of harmful bacteria is simply to increase the numbers of beneficial bacteria. Increasing the amount of fibre we consume in our diet is believed to be a good method for achieving that goal. Of course, we should not expect this to have any immediate ameliorative effect on a possible infection with *E. coli 0157* bacteria.

An Increase in Colonic Polyps and Colon Cancer

PRESIDENT IKEDA: We often hear nowadays that more and more people are suffering from colonic polyps. What exactly are polyps?

UEHIGASHI: A polyp is a small growth, like a tiny mushroom, that forms on mucous membranes. Colonic polyps appear on the wall of the colon (the large intestine).

PRESIDENT IKEDA: Is there a link between polyps and cancer?

UEHIGASHI: By far the majority of polyps are benign and no cause for real concern. But there are also polyps, even small ones, that are cancerous or have the potential for becoming cancerous in the future. Moreover, when they are small, we do not experience any symptoms and so are not aware of them. Quick diagnosis and removal, therefore, are the key.

TOYOFUKU: Those over forty, who have entered the so-called 'cancer years' should make a point of having a thorough annual medical check-up.

PRESIDENT IKEDA: Are there any preventative measures we can take?

UEHIGASHI: The most important one is to improve our diet. We should reduce our intake of fat and animal protein and increase our intake of high-fibre foods, such as vegetables, whole grains, potatoes, legumes and seaweeds.

MORITA: The increasing westernization of the Japanese lifestyle is widely thought to be behind the recent increase in colonic polyps and colon cancer in Japan.

The Astonishing Surface Area and Functions of the Small Intestine

PRESIDENT IKEDA: In addition to the colon or large intestine, the intestinal tract includes the duodenum and the small intestine.

TOYOFUKU: Yes. *Duodenum* means 'twelve-finger' breadth. The duodenum, which connects to the stomach, is so named because its length is about the size of the combined width of twelve fingers.

MORITA: The small intestine, which is in turn connected to the duodenum, is about six to seven metres (twenty to twenty-six feet) in length when stretched out straight. The large intestine or colon, which follows after the small intestine, is only 1.6 to 1.7 metres (five to five-and-a-half feet).

PRESIDENT IKEDA: So the small intestine is actually large, and the large intestine small! Did the large intestine get its name from its width, then?

TOYOFUKU: Yes. The large intestine is twice as wide in diameter as the small intestine, ranging from five to eight centimetres (two to three inches).

UEHIGASHI: The primary function of the small intestine is to absorb nutrients, while that of the large intestine is to absorb water. The long length of the small intestine ensures that all of the nutrients in the food we eat can be fully absorbed.

PRESIDENT IKEDA: I have heard that if all its creases and folds were flattened out, the small intestine would cover an area approximately the size of two tennis courts.

TOYOFUKU: The walls of the small intestine are covered with what are known as mucosal villi, tiny projections like the pile of a carpet. There are thought to be as many as thirty million villi on the walls of the small intestine. Nutrients are absorbed through the surface of the villi. If the surfaces of all the villi were flattened out, they would indeed cover an area of that size.

PRESIDENT IKEDA: It is true as if there is an enormous 'palace' inside our bodies. This vast surface area absorbs every morsel of nutrition we consume. How awesome are the workings of the human body!

I have even heard that when some foreign object is mistakenly ingested — say, for example, a piece of glass — the instant the sharp edge of the glass comes into contact with the intestinal wall, the glass is flipped over and its orientation changed so that it can do no further harm.

MORITA: Even though we may not be aware of it, our body is always doing its best to preserve this precious gift of life.

Does Eating Water Melon Seeds Cause Appendicitis?

PRESIDENT IKEDA: By the way, Dr Uehigashi, have you ever had appendicitis?

UEHIGASHI: I am afraid not.

TOYOFUKU: I would say that was quite fortunate!

PRESIDENT IKEDA: Where exactly in the intestinal tract is the appendix located?

UEHIGASHI: It is located where the small intestine connects to the large intestine. A narrow sac about five to seven centimetres (two to three inches) in length hangs from this connection. Appendicitis refers to an inflammation of the appendix.

PRESIDENT IKEDA: According to Japanese folk wisdom, swallowing grape or water melon seeds causes appendicitis. Is that true?

MORITA: It is true that on rare occasions fruit seeds are found in an appendix that has been surgically removed. But this may simply be because once the appendix became inflamed, it was no longer able to expel fruit seeds that found their way into it. Appendicitis can occur when nothing at all is in the appendix. So, I think we can say that eating fruit seeds will not necessarily cause appendicitis.

PRESIDENT IKEDA: Appendicitis is not the only intestinal illness that causes abdominal pain, is it?

UEHIGASHI: Actually, the most common intestinal disorder is acute enteritis (inflammation of the small intestine). Over-indulging in food and drinks, and antibiotics can also cause this condition.

On rare occasions fruit seeds are found in an appendix that has been surgically removed. But this may simply be because once the appendix became inflamed, it was no longer able to expel fruit seeds that found their way into it. Appendicitis can occur when nothing at all is in the appendix. So, we can say that eating fruit seeds will not necessarily cause appendicitis.

TOYOFUKU: Food poisoning, as well as contagious diseases, such as typhoid and dysentery, can also cause abdominal pain.

PRESIDENT IKEDA: What about chronic, rather than acute, enteritis?

UEHIGASHI: Ulcerative colitis and Crohn's disease typically manifest themselves as chronic enteritis or colitis (inflammation of the colon). Ulcerative colitis is a condition in which many small bleeding ulcers form on the mucous membrane of the colon. In Crohn's disease, on the other hand, much deeper ulcers form not only in the colon, but in the small intestine and the stomach as well. Both diseases are usually accompanied by a bloody and mucous-filled diarrhoea.

PRESIDENT IKEDA: What are the causes?

UEHIGASHI: We do not know the precise causes, but stress and exhaustion can tend to aggravate both conditions.

The Intestines are Very Sensitive to Our Emotional State

TOYOFUKU: Like the stomach, the intestines are very sensitive to emotional and mental states. For example, we are likely to become constipated when we are travelling and find ourselves in a strange environment, or when strong stress continues for an extended period of time, such as studying for school entrance examinations. And children, are especially sensitive. A harsh scolding, for instance, can cause them to suffer from diarrhoea.

PRESIDENT IKEDA: Isn't there also a stress-related intestinal disorder characterised by persistent diarrhoea or constipation?

MORITA: Yes. It is known as irritable bowel syndrome.

PRESIDENT IKEDA: There is a saying that the intestines are the mirror of the mind. And in Japan, the word for the intestines and other internal organs (*harawata* or *cho* — the reading depending on the context) is used in many expressions to mean the mind or one's emotional or mental state.

When we say someone's 'bowels are rotten' (*harawata ga chigireru*) means to be in a state of unbearable agony or sadness.

MORITA: We also have the expression, "as if one's bowels are being cut," (*dancho no omoi*), which has a similar meaning to the latter, doesn't it?

PRESIDENT IKEDA: Yes. That expression reminds me of the story of a faithful minister named Hung Yen of the kingdom of Wei in ancient China. While Hung Yen was on a mission to another kingdom, his lord, Duke Yi, was attacked and killed by an enemy. The body was mutilated and the internal organs strewn here and there.

By the time Hung Yen returned to Wei, all that was left of the Duke was his liver. Weeping tears of bitter grief, Hung Yen sacrificed his own life so as to hide his master's shame, cutting open his own stomach, pulling out his intestines, and placing Duke Yi's liver inside his own body.

Nichiren Daishonin referred to the story of Hung Yen as an example of true loyalty, using it to praise the bravery of Shijo Kingo, who .was ready to die with the Daishonin in a terrible persecution.

In the Gosho, The Persecution at Tatsunokuchi, *the Daishonin writes to Shijo Kingo: "You accompanied Nichiren, vowing to give your life as a votary of the Lotus Sutra. Your deed is a hundred, thousand, ten thousand times greater than that of Hung Yen, who cut open his stomach and inserted the liver of his dead lord, Duke Yi, [to save him from shame and dishonour]."* (WND, pg 196)

It Takes about Forty-eight Hours to Digest Our Food

PRESIDENT IKEDA: When we eat, the food travels a long, winding path down our esophagus, into the stomach, and through the small intestines, before undigested waste matter finally passes into the bowel for expulsion. About how long does the food we ingest remain in our bodies?

TOYOFUKU: The entire digestive process in a healthy person is said to be an average of forty-eight hours.

MORITA: Constipation or diarrhoea are signs that the natural rhythm has been somehow disrupted.

PRESIDENT IKEDA: What is the best treatment for diarrhoea?

UEHIGASHI: When severe diarrhoea continues too long, there is cause for concern, since it can lead to dehydration. In such cases, it is important to drink plenty of liquids that are around the same temperature as our normal body temperature, such as lukewarm tea, to replenish the body's water supply.

TOYOFUKU: And, one should also eat foods that do not upset or overstimulate the intestinal tract. High-fibre foods, fat, spices, and alcohol should all be avoided, as should cold drinks, such as carbonated soft drinks.

PRESIDENT IKEDA: Is there anything we should know about over-the-counter diarrhoea medicines?

UEHIGASHI: In some cases, diarrhoea is the body's attempt to expel toxic matter as quickly as possible. As a result, when diarrhoea is caused by food poisoning or overindulging in food or drinks, trying to stop it with medicine can in fact make the situation worse.

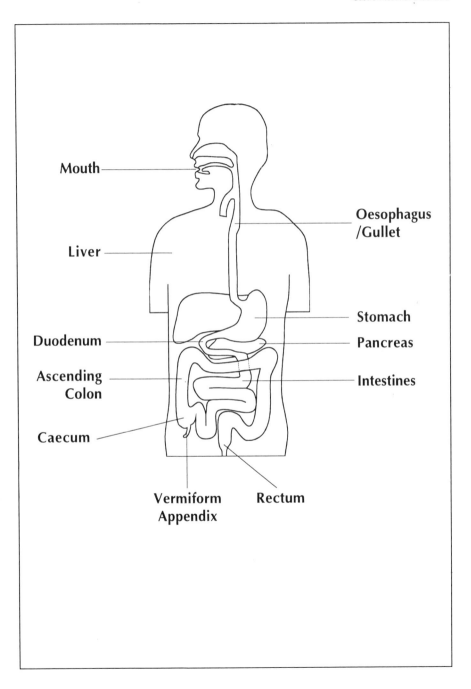

MORITA: When the patient has a fever or is vomiting, or when diarrhoea persists for a long time, it is best to go and see a doctor without delay and find out the cause.

PRESIDENT IKEDA: Many people also seems to suffer from constipation. How many days without a bowel movement qualifies as constipation?

UEHIGASHI: Each individual has a different level at which he or she feels constipated. When a person has a regular rhythm of good bowel movements, even if it is only one in two or three days, we do not regard it as constipation. The problems arise when a patient feels as if the stomach is distended, loses appetite, or feels as if bowel movements are not complete. Other changes in bowel movements that are cause for concern are a hardening of the stool, requiring more time to pass it out, or a sudden decrease in the frequency of bowel movement from, for example, once a day to once in three or four days.

PRESIDENT IKEDA: Can chronic constipation be caused by disease?

UEHIGASHI: Yes, it can. Inflammation or malignant tumours in the large intestine can cause constipation. If you have stubborn constipation, you should see a doctor. If the results of the examination show that it is not caused by any disease, then it is time to start reviewing your lifestyle for possible causes and to make changes where necessary.

PRESIDENT IKEDA: What points of our lifestyle should we review?

UEHIGASHI: Start with your daily rhythm. The human body is built so that when food enters the stomach, it stimulates the bowels to movement. Being aware of this will help you achieve regular bowel movements. It is equally important to develop a rhythm where you do not ignore signals that indicate the body is ready for a bowel movement.

MORITA: What frequently happens, however, is that people get up late in the morning and do not have the time to eat. Or even if they do have time for breakfast, they have to rush off for the train to work or school, so even should they feel the desire for a bowel movement, they are forced to wait.

UEHIGASHI: Precisely. Though you feel the natural need for a bowel movement, you have to wait, which interrupts your natural rhythm. The first step in preventing constipation is to eat three meals daily on a regular schedule and establish a predictable rhythm for your stomach and bowels.

TOYOFUKU: It is also a good idea to drink plenty of liquids, because water tends to soften the stool. Drinking a glass of water or milk soon after you wake up in the morning can be effective.

Medicines are a Temporary Resort

MORITA: Lack of exercise is also a cause of constipation. If you lack regular exercise for an extended period of time, the functions of the autonomic nervous system that coordinates the activities of the digestive system are disrupted. That can cause a disruption in normal bowel function.

PRESIDENT IKEDA: What items of our diet should we pay attention to?

> **Overuse of laxatives and enemas in fact often contributes to a weakening of bowel function. Once you have returned to your natural rhythm, you should stop using laxatives.**

UEHIGASHI: Eating too much protein and starch to the exclusion of vegetable fibre, which makes up a large portion of the stool, will slow down the activities of the bowel. In contrast to diarrhoea, when you are constipated you should eat plenty of vegetables and fruits, seaweed and mushrooms, which are all high in fibre.

PRESIDENT IKEDA: Some people seem to make constant use of laxatives.

UEHIGASHI: Overuse of laxatives and enemas in fact often contributes to a weakening of bowel function. Once you have returned to your natural rhythm, you should stop using laxatives.

Again, for people who are middle-aged and older, the sudden onset of chronic constipation can be a sign of cancer in the intestinal tract. In such cases, laxatives may offer temporary relief but actually prevent the patient from investigating the true cause of the constipation and delaying the diagnosis of cancer.

Toyofuku: Treatment of constipation should be based on paying careful attention to one's daily habits, and drugs should only be employed as a temporary measure. The more stubborn the constipation is, the greater patience and determination will be required to control it.

Happiness and Joy Stimulate the Intestines

President Ikeda: I have heard the saying, "The intestines rule the world." It may sound a little strange, but I think the meaning is that individual human beings are ruled by the health of their intestines, and human beings rule the world. Our intestines are the part of our bodies that extract from the food we eat and the energy we need to live, and go about our daily activities. They are the source of our strength and vitality. If our intestinal tract is not healthy and active, we can not be healthy and active, either.

In addition to taking care of our health, however, we must also remember to be cheerful and have a positive attitude towards life. It is said that happiness makes the intestines active, while sadness and depression slow them down. Since we have been given the gift of life, we must live it vibrantly and to the fullest. Since we are advancing on our journey through life everyday, we may as well do it with joy and excitement.

The fatigue that we have accumulated over the summer months will now start to make itself felt in earnest. I hope that all of our readers will become 'doctors' who can tend to their own inner well-being, acting in the best interests for their physical and mental health, so that they can enjoy a wonderful, fulfilling autumn.

Heart Disease

Participants in this discussion on
' Humanism and the Art of Medicine:
A New Century of Health'
are SGI President Ikeda, Soka Gakkai
Doctors' Division Leaders
Dr Shuhei Morita and Dr Hiroyuki Toyofuku,
along with special guest, Chiba Prefecture
Doctors' Division Leader Yasuo Imazeki

PRESIDENT IKEDA: Heart disease is frightening, isn't it? It can strike so suddenly and unexpectedly. I believe it is now the second leading cause of death in Japan next to cancer.

MORITA: That is true. In other parts of the industrialised world, such as Europe and the United States, the death rate from heart disease is even higher than in Japan.
Most cases of sudden death are also caused by heart disease.

PRESIDENT IKEDA: Joining us today is Dr Imazeki, a heart specialist. I am sure we will have many questions for him on this subject, which I know will be one of great interest to our readers.

IMAZEKI: I will certainly do my best to be of assistance.

PRESIDENT IKEDA: I think it is fair to say that for many people, a white coat and a stethoscope are the very symbols of a doctor. A stethoscope allows you to hear the heartbeat, doesn't it?

IMAZEKI: Yes, we can hear the heart valves opening and closing. We can also hear irregular noises, such as heart murmurs. The stethoscope looks like a very simple piece of equipment, but it is indispensable in examining the heart for irregularities.

PRESIDENT IKEDA: Who invented the stethoscope?

TOYOFUKU: René T.H. Laënnec (1781-1826), a French physician, is credited with its invention.

IMAZEKI: There is an interesting story about how Laënnec came to invent the stethoscope. Up until that time, doctors listened to the heart by pressing their ear directly against the patient's chest. Then one day, a rather plump young woman who thought she had heart problems came to visit Dr Laënnec. Unfortunately, he could not hear her heart very well. The doctor, young himself, was embarrassed to press his ear against the patient's chest.

MORITA: He was quite a gentleman, it seems.

IMAZEKI: And that is how he came to invent the stethoscope.

PRESIDENT IKEDA: I see. So, his consideration for a female patient led to an invaluable invention.

Are there any other ways to check for heart irregularities?

IMAZEKI: Yes, by taking a person's pulse.

PRESIDENT IKEDA: You usually check the pulse at the wrist, don't you?

IMAZEKI: Yes. Even more effective in checking for heart irregularities is an electrocardiogram (ECG). And, ECG will reveal most heart problems, including arrhythmias (irregular heartbeat) and the presence of coronary heart disease that could lead to angina and heart attack.

The Heart: A Powerful Pump

PRESIDENT IKEDA: The shape of the heart actually resembles its conventional depiction — as the hearts in a deck of cards, for instance — doesn't it?

IMAZEKI: Yes. The pointed end of the heart faces downward.

PRESIDENT IKEDA: The Chinese character for heart is also a representation of the heart's shape. In ancient India, the heart was compared to a lotus flower. In medical texts from that time, its shape is described as resembling the lotus bud, with the tip of the bud drooping downward. Exactly how large is the heart?

IMAZEKI: In most cases, our heart is just a bit larger than our fist, and varies accordingly from one individual to another. It does an astonishing amount of work for its size, though. The heart is a pump that circulates blood throughout the body. In one day, it pumps approximately 8,000 litres (2,000 gallons) of blood.

TOYOFUKU: That is about forty 200-litre (50 gallons) drum cans of liquid.

PRESIDENT IKEDA: The heart is a real little dynamo, isn't it! Being a pump, then, the heart displays rhythmical contractions. When it contracts, I guess, blood is pumped out, and when it relaxes, blood flows in. Am I right?

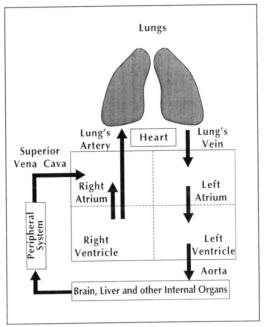

Diagram: The Blood Flow.

IMAZEKI: That is how it works. The blood pumped by the heart transports oxygen and nutrients to every part of the body while carrying away carbon dioxide and other waste products.

MORITA: When the body is at rest, the heart usually beats at a rate ranging from sixty to eighty times a minute, or about 100,000 times a day. The heart muscle pumps continuously and at a regular rhythm, never resting.

TOYOFUKU: In a lifetime of eighty years, for instance, the heart would beat more than two billion times.

PRESIDENT IKEDA: It is amazing that it does not tire, beating continually and without interruption as it does from birth to death. Of course, I am not saying it should take time out to rest!

Is the heart made of some special material?

IMAZEKI: It certainly is. It is made up of a unique kind of muscle tissue different from that of any other muscles in the body. Skeletal muscles, like those in our arms and legs, are known as voluntary muscles because we have conscious control over them. These muscles perform very efficiently but also tire relatively easily. Smooth muscles, such as those in the walls of our intestines, are called involuntary muscles because we have no conscious control over them. This type of muscle does not tire easily. Heart muscle exhibits rhythmic contraction and combines the twin features of being both efficient and untiring.

PRESIDENT IKEDA: To sum this up, then, the muscles of our internal organs are always working at a slow and steady pace and do not tire easily, while the muscles of our arms and legs are capable of great burst of energy but tire easily. (People seem to come in these two types, too!) And the heart, which combines the best of both types of muscles, is the cornerstone that maintains our life.

MORITA: That is right. Even more astonishing is the fact that throughout their lifetime, the cells of the heart muscle (myocardium) are not replaced with new cells.

Angina and Heart Attack

TOYOFUKU: Though the heart is by nature indefatigable, it sometimes suffers from problems and irregularities. These we call heart disease.

PRESIDENT IKEDA: What are the main kinds of heart disorders?

IMAZEKI: The most common forms are angina (angina pectoris) and heart attack (myocardial infarction). In both cases, there is a narrowing or blockage of a coronary artery that supplies blood to the heart, so that the heart does not receive sufficient oxygen and nutrients.

TOYOFUKU: Angina refers to a condition in which there is temporary reduction of oxygen supply to the heart muscle caused by the narrowing of diseased coronary arteries. Heart attack, or myocardial infarction, describes a more serious situation. It occurs when a coronary artery is obstructed by a clot, and blood is no longer able to flow past it, causing the cells beyond that point to die.

PRESIDENT IKEDA: *Infarction* means 'obstruction', doesn't it?

MORITA: Yes. A cerebral infarction, or stroke, refers to a condition where the arteries are blocked and blood is prevented from circulating to the brain.

PRESIDENT IKEDA: We might describe angina as when the heart has difficulty 'breathing', and heart attack as the heart's 'suffocation'.

TOYOFUKU: Yes. And, it is indeed ironic that the heart, which delivers oxygen and nutrients throughout the body, should itself suffer from a depletion of blood and, consequently, oxygen and nutrients.

PRESIDENT IKEDA: Why is it that the arteries narrow?

IMAZEKI: It is mainly caused by what we call arteriosclerosis, a hardening or narrowing of the arteries, which sharply restricts the flow of blood that can pass through them. It is caused by an accumulation of cholesterol and other substances on the inner walls of the arteries, which leads to a variety of changes, including a thickening of the artery walls.

MORITA: The most common causes· of arteriosclerosis are hyperlipemia (the excess presence of lipids or cholesterol in the blood), diabetes, high blood pressure, cigarette smoking and obesity.

TOYOFUKU: In addition to arteriosclerosis, coronary vasospasms (spasms of coronary arteries) can also restrict the flow of blood to the heart.

PRESIDENT IKEDA: What are the symptoms of angina?

IMAZEKI: A pressing tightness and dull pain in the chest. This can happen during exercise or when climbing stairs, and then go away after resting.
   When vasospasms are the cause, the pain is usually felt when sleeping or just as one gets out of bed.

TOYOFUKU: The root meaning of the English word *angina* is 'to strangle'. The name comes from the nature of the pain of angina, which feels as if the heart were being strangled.

MORITA: The discomfort is not felt just around the heart. It can be felt all across the chest area.

IMAZEKI: Yes, angina sometimes radiates as far as the solar plexus back, shoulders, jaw, teeth and neck.

PRESIDENT IKEDA: How long does an attack usually last?

IMAZEKI: If you immediately stop to rest, it usually passes in two or three minutes. The longest it will last is about ten to fifteen minutes. But angina is a warning sign of coronary heart disease that could lead to heart attack. It is important to recognise it as such and get it checked out by one's doctor.

Heart Attacks Frequently Occur in the Morning

PRESIDENT IKEDA: What are the symptoms of heart attack?

IMAZEKI: As in angina, one experiences chest pain, only more intense and usually accompanied by an acute sense of fear and apprehension. The pain lasts longer, sometimes for several hours.

It is vital to get to a hospital as quickly as possible, preferably one that has a properly equipped coronary care unit. Many of those who suffer from acute heart attack die within the first few hours.

PRESIDENT IKEDA: Is there any time of day during which heart attacks are more likely to occur?

IMAZEKI: Most attacks occur between six and ten o'clock in the morning. Eight to ten in the evening is another dangerous period. Though it is true that sharp pain is a typical symptom of heart attack, on rare occasions there is no pain at all.

PRESIDENT IKEDA: That is an important point to keep in mind.

IMAZEKI: Older victims, in particular, often do not feel any severe chest pain and can actually have a heart attack with no more than lethargy, difficulty in breathing and loss of appetite as the symptoms.

Earlier, I noted that angina is a warning sign for coronary heart disease that can lead to heart attack, but not every heart attack is preceded by angina. One can have a heart attack quite suddenly, without any warning. As a result, we should not think we are safe just because we do not manifest any of the typical symptoms. Even without symptoms, it is important to have regular check-ups.

MORITA: Yet, there are those with the symptoms who do not see their doctor.

TOYOFUKU: They must have strong hearts!

PRESIDENT IKEDA: It is our responsibility to look after our health. We should have regular check-ups, not put them off because we are afraid of what the doctor might find or just because we feel they are a nuisance.

> **This life is precious. It is a life with mission. There would surely be nothing sadder than failing to accomplish one's mission because of carelessly neglecting to take care of one's health or taking the arrogant attitude of "I'm all right."**

This life is precious. It is a life with mission. There would surely be nothing sadder than failing to accomplish one's mission because of carelessly neglecting to take care of one's health or taking the arrogant attitude of "I'm all right."

Nichiren Daishonin rejoiced that his follower, Shijo Kingo, managed to survive a dangerous situation, listing three reasons why the latter had been able to do so. They were 'prudence', 'courage' and 'firm faith in the Lotus Sutra'. Precisely because we are practising the Daishonin's Buddhism, it is essential that we demonstrate the qualities of prudence and courage as an integral part of our lives.

In The Strategy of the Lotus Sutra, *the Daishonin writes, "It is a matter of rejoicing that your usual prudence and courage, as well as your firm faith in the Lotus Sutra, enabled you to survive unharmed." (MW-I-245)*

Heart Failure is a Decline in the Heart's Pumping Ability

PRESIDENT IKEDA: We often hear the term 'heart failure'. What exactly does it refer to?

IMAZEKI: Heart failure refers to a condition in which the pumping ability of the heart is weakened. The heart cannot pump sufficient blood to meet the body's needs, resulting in a lack of oxygen and nutrients being supplied to the body.

PRESIDENT IKEDA: What is the cause?

IMAZEKI: It can be caused by some change in the heart muscle resulting from a heart attack or some other disorder, which leads to a weakening of cardiac function.

TOYOFUKU: High blood pressure is another major cause. When a person has high blood pressure, the heart has to work harder than it should in order to pump blood through blood vessels, which places a heavy burden on the heart.

IMAZEKI: Valvular heart disease is another condition that overtaxes the heart. There are four valves that open and shut when the heart pumps blood. When a person suffers from valvular heart disease, these valves do not open and shut correctly. And when its' valves do not function properly, the heart cannot pump as much blood as it should.

PRESIDENT IKEDA: What are the symptoms of heart failure?

IMAZEKI: The most conspicuous early symptoms are shortness of breath and coughing. At first, these are only noticeable when exercising, but eventually they also occur when the patient is at rest, and breathing becomes difficult.

TOYOFUKU: Fatigue, lethargy and loss of appetite are also symptoms. These are caused by insufficient blood being pumped around the body to meet its needs.

MORITA: When blood circulation throughout the body is poor, blood starts to accumulate in various parts of the body, and the patient may experience swelling (edema) of the arms and legs and weight gain (as a result of sodium and fluid retention).

IMAZEKI: Anyone who experiences these symptoms should see a physician without delay.

Irregular Heart Rhythm

PRESIDENT IKEDA: Some people experience skipped or irregular heart beats. What does that mean?

IMAZEKI: These are a sign of arrhythmias. As the name reveals, this describes a syndrome in which the rhythm of the heart's contraction is irregular, suddenly racing or slowing down.

MORITA: It does not, of course, refer to the speeding up of the pulse as a normal reaction, such as when we exercise or are surprised.

PRESIDENT IKEDA: So even the heart, with its wonderful capabilities, can get out of rhythm?

IMAZEKI: Perhaps after working so unfailingly for so many years, it cannot help but miss a beat every once in a while! But seriously, though an irregular pulse may be discomforting, there is no reason to be overly worried about this condition. In most cases, treatment is unnecessary. What is of the essence here is determining whether the irregular pulse warrants treatment or not.

PRESIDENT IKEDA: When should we pay special attention to irregular pulse?

IMAZEKI: Simply speaking, when, in a resting state, the pulse beats more than 100 times or less than forty times per minute, or when the pulse alternately speeds up and then slows down.

PRESIDENT IKEDA: What causes this?

IMAZEKI: It can be caused by underlying heart disorders, such as angina or heart attack, or by diseases unrelated to the heart, such as anaemia and thyroid disorders.

MORITA: Lifestyle also plays a big role. Many factors, such as exhaustion, lack of sleep, stress, excessive cigarette smoking and drinking too much coffee can unnaturally stimulate and overwork the heart.

PRESIDENT IKEDA: What kind of symptoms might someone suffering from arrhythmias experience in his or her daily life?

IMAZEKI: Palpitations and a feeling of faintness are possible symptoms. Some people worry too much about arrhythmias. But if you visit a reliable, expert physician and are told you have nothing to worry about, it is better not to pay too much attention to irregular heart rhythms. In fact, worrying about it too much can increase your anxiety so much so that the symptoms are actually worsened.

PRESIDENT IKEDA: Perhaps, we can think of the heart as the 'sun' of the inner universe or microcosm of our body.

The sun provides life-giving energy to all things. If the sun's light were to weaken even to a small degree, it would have potentially deadly consequences for all life.

Similarly, the heart is also central to the body, providing oxygen and nutrients to all its parts. If the heart is healthy and vigorous, all the cells of the body can perform their functions with vigour.

In the Buddhist sutras, the heart nestled between the right and left lungs is likened to the image of an eight petalled lotus flower. And, when Nichiren Daishonin correlates the parts of our body to *Myoho-renge-kyo*, he says, *"ren* (lotus flower) is the chest." (*Gosho Zenshu*, pg 716) Since ancient time, the lotus flower has also been a symbol of the sun.

What should we do to keep this sun of our body and our life in good shape? And, what steps can we take to prevent heart disease?

IMAZEKI: Well, for starters, one should do a quick self-check for the symptoms of heart disease.

PRESIDENT IKEDA: Can you review those symptoms for us once again?

IMAZEKI: The main signs of heart disease are chest pain, palpitations, shortness of breath, edema (swelling due to fluid retention) and dizziness. Of course, these can be symptoms of other illnesses as well.

PRESIDENT IKEDA: Please tell our readers how they can distinguish whether such symptoms might be signs of heart disease or some other illness.

IMAZEKI: It is difficult to make a clear distinction, but I will endeavour to offer some general points that might serve as a basic guideline.

As far as chest pain is concerned, angina is characterised by a dull pain and tightness — as if the heart is being strangled. In a heart attack, the pain is more intense and usually accompanied by a sense of anxiety or panic. In the latter case, the pain is felt deep in the chest over an area larger than the palm of one's hand.

MORITA: The source of the pain in heart disease is hard to locate. One cannot point directly to it; instead, one has a vague feeling the pain is concentrated around a certain area.

> **A pain on the left side of the chest does not necessarily indicate a heart problem. Neuralgia (acute nerve pain) is often mistaken for heart pain. In the cases of angina and heart attack, chest pain is often accompanied — at the same time or just a bit later — by pain, heaviness or numbness in other parts of the body, such as the arms and shoulders, the neck, jaw, teeth, and behind the ear.**

TOYOFUKU: In the case of other diseases, chest pain is more likely to be a quick, sharp pain, or a prickling pain on the surface of the chest, or a throbbing pain.

IMAZEKI: A pain on the left side of the chest does not necessarily indicate a heart problem. Neuralgia (acute nerve pain) is often mistaken for heart pain. In the cases of angina and heart attack, chest pain is often accompanied — at the same time or just a bit later — by pain, heaviness or numbness in other parts of the body, such as the arms and shoulders, the neck, jaw, teeth, and behind the ear.

PRESIDENT IKEDA: What about palpitations?

IMAZEKI: If you have previously never experienced palpitations but suddenly start to feel them after walking briskly or after just a few steps up a stairway, there is a chance that they could be indications of heart disease. If you experience them when at rest, you may have arrhythmias (irregular heart rhythms). Of course, we must remember that even healthy people may experience palpitations if they get up from a sleeping position too quickly or are suffering from fatigue or lack of exercise.

MORITA: The same is true of shortness of breath. When you can no longer climb a flight of stairs or a hill that presented no problem in the past, there is a possibility that you are suffering from heart failure. If the symptoms worsen, you may find yourself short of breath even when you are not exerting yourself.

PRESIDENT IKEDA: One of the symptoms of heart was edema, wasn't it?

IMAZEKI: Yes. Kidney disease is also characterised by edema, but in the case of heart disease, the edema usually starts from the lower body.

PRESIDENT IKEDA: Tell us something about the dizziness that can be caused by heart disease.

IMAZEKI: Dizziness (also known as vertigo) is usually caused by standing up too quickly from a sitting or lying down position or by Meniere's syndrome (an inner ear disorder marked by recurrent bouts of dizziness, ringing in the ears and deafness). Dizziness associated with heart disease is usually caused by arrhythmias. It occurs suddenly and without warning, and one feels weak and faint.

PRESIDENT IKEDA: Of all heart disorders, I think those leading to angina and heart attack are probably the most frightening.

TOYOFUKU: Yes. Angina and heart attack are the result of what is called ischemic heart disease, because they are caused by insufficient blood inflow (ischemia) to the heart muscle (the myocardium). Roughly seventy per cent of all sudden deaths caused by heart disease can be attributed to ischemic heart disease.

PRESIDENT IKEDA: What can we do to guard against it?

IMAZEKI: There are several risk factors that can contribute to ischemic heart disease.

MORITA: To put it simply, they are all harmful things that put an added load on the heart.

PRESIDENT IKEDA: For example?

IMAZEKI: Hyperlipemia (high levels of lipids in the blood), smoking, high blood pressure, diabetes, obesity and stress are major risk factors in heart disease. Even though you may have none of the symptoms I mentioned earlier, if you have any of these risk factors you need to be alert to the possibility of heart disease. Even one of these factors represents a danger; if you have two or three, the greater the risk of developing heart disease.

TOYOFUKU: Fortunately, most of these risk factors can be eliminated or reduced by improving one's habits and lifestyle. Removing even one of these added burdens to your heart significantly reduces your risk of heart disease.

The Harm of Smoking

IMAZEKI: Hyperlipemia, high blood pressure, diabetes and obesity all lead to arteriosclerosis (a hardening and narrowing of the arteries), which is one of the main causes of ischemic heart disease.

PRESIDENT IKEDA: Arteriosclerosis is a condition in which cholesterol or other substances accumulate in the arteries, causing their walls to thicken.

IMAZEKI: Yes. The resulting narrowing of the arterial channels hinders good blood circulation.

TOYOFUKU: Smoking also contributes to arteriosclerosis.

PRESIDENT IKEDA: Those with heart disease should refrain from smoking, then?

IMAZEKI: Yes. Smokers have two to three times the incidence of angina and heart attack that non-smokers do. By quitting smoking, you can reduce by half in only one year the likelihood of ischemic heart disease.

PRESIDENT IKEDA: Are ischemic diseases that lead to angina and heart attack genetic? Do we inherit them?

IMAZEKI: No, they are not inherited diseases as such. But if you have a parent or a sibling with ischemic heart disease, you should regard yourself as susceptible as well, because you probably have a similar lifestyle and dietary habits.

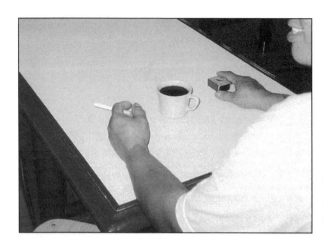

Smokers have two to three times the incidence of angina and heart attack that non-smokers do.

The Characteristics of the 'Type A' Personality

MORITA: Stress also places a great burden on the heart. The 'Type A' personality, which is especially susceptible to stress, is believed to be vulnerable to ischemic heart disease.

PRESIDENT IKEDA: What do you mean by 'Type A personality'? Is it the same as blood-type category?

IMAZEKI: No, it has no relation to a person's blood type. It is a simple division of human personalities into Type A and Type B.

PRESIDENT IKEDA: What are the actual characteristics of the Type A personality?

IMAZEKI: Some Type A personality traits are a strong sense of responsibility, competitiveness, a driven nature, a strong need for social approval and a tendency to be easily irritated and annoyed, among others.

TOYOFUKU: Type A individuals tend to believe that they have to work hard to be valued, to demonstrate the worth of their existence. That is why this type of person is always so competitive.

Morita: In Japan, we used to call such people 'superworkers' or 'corporate warriors'.

Being Satisfied with Our Life

President Ikeda: Naturally, working and being busy are not in themselves unhealthy. The problem is the motivation that drives you, what it is that you are working for, isn't it? Of course, here I am not talking about overexerting yourself past a reasonable point. It is just that if you are always seeking the approval of others, you are, in a way, a slave to public opinion. You are controlled by the opinions of others and have no life of your own. You aren't living your own life. You may be a success, but when you grow older you will experience a feeling of emptiness, of dissatisfaction. A life measured by the opinions of others, which are arbitrary and always changing, will be essentially insecure. You will have no peace of mind.

I think that such insecurity and anxiety — rather than the mere fact of being busy — are what destroy physical and mental health. They say that a machine doesn't break down from continual operation, but that it is the constant friction that eventually wears it down and causes it to stop. Worry and stress are the 'friction' of human life.

The secret is to have strong faith and be in control of your life. Success in society is certainly a good thing, but what matters most is whether you have achieved your personal goals and can say that you are satisfied with your life, whether or not others appreciate or recognise what you have accomplished. That is the kind of life to live. If you have that kind of faith and sense of mission, you may be very busy and active, but all your activity will have a positive, energising effect on your body and mind.

Morita: As the Daishonin says, what matters most is one's heart.

Warm Human Ties can Prevent Heart Disease

Morita: I have heard a very interesting story regarding heart disease.[1] It took

---

1. Source: Andrew Weil, MD, *Spontaneous Healing: How to Discover and Enhance Your Body's Natural Ability to Maintain and Heal Itself* (New York: Fawcett Columbine, 1995), pg 208-209.

SGI President Ikeda (2nd right) , Soka Gakkai Doctors' Division Leaders Dr Shuhei Morita (2nd left) and Dr Hiroyuki Toyofuku (right), along with special guest, Chiba Prefecture Doctors' Division Leader Yasuo Imazeki (left) in discussion.

place in the town of Roseto, in Pennsylvania. Roseto was founded by Italian immigrants in the 1930s. Most of the people in the town were great eaters. Their diet had a high content of fat and meat, and many of them were smokers, too. Yet, very few of the town's residents died of ischemic heart disease.

In searching for the reason for this medical oddity, it was discovered that the town was like one big, happy, good natured family bound together by a spirit of mutual concern and deep personal interaction among neighbours. There were many customs and institutions that gave residents chances to get together, communicate and enjoy one another's company. In other words, the strong personal ties among the town's residents seemed to be somehow linked to the lower-than-expected incidence of heart disease.

Time passed, and by the time the children of the original residents reached adulthood, the old way of doing things had given way to nuclear families, and the link of each individual to the community as a whole was weakened. Roseto's fine tradition of neighbourliness was disappearing. As a result, though the diet remained the same as in the past, the rate of ischemic heart disease gradually rose to the US average.

PRESIDENT IKEDA: This anecdote may not be conclusive, but it does seem that loneliness, alienation and despair can have a negative influence on the heart. A large amount of data supports this. Communication, open-hearted sharing and dialogue can have tremendous healing power.

TOYOFUKU: In that sense, the SGI represents a healing oasis in our troubled world.

Diet and Exercise

PRESIDENT IKEDA: What areas of our daily lives should we pay special attention to if we want to reduce the risk factors for heart disease?

MORITA: As far as diet is concerned, the standard advice prevails: eat regular, balanced meals, refrain from overeating and reduce sodium intake.

PRESIDENT IKEDA: Some say that eating large quantities of meat isn't good for the heart. Is that true?

IMAZEKI: The problem is not meat *per se* but animal fat, particularly beef and pork fat. But meat is an excellent source of protein. A lack of animal protein can lead to weak and prematurely ageing arteries. The key is to eliminate as much of the fat from meat as possible. This can be done by selecting lean cuts and employing cooking methods that get rid of or reduce the fat, such as grilling.

MORITA: Fish provide animal protein and there does not seem to be any problem with the oils in fish.

TOYOFUKU: That is true. Certain kinds of fish we eat in Japan, such as sardines and mackerel, are fatty, but it is believed their oils actually lower cholesterol.

PRESIDENT IKEDA: I believe research indicates that certain components found in fish oil actually help prevent blood clots.[2]

Earlier you mentioned that smoking is bad for the heart, but what about alcohol?

IMAZEKI: Taken in moderate amounts, alcohol may actually help prevent arteriosclerosis.

---

2. The beneficial components found in fish oils are eicosapentaenoic acid (EPA) and docosahexaenoic acid (DHA).

President Ikeda: Really? I am sure that news will make many people very happy!

Imazeki: Remember, I said 'in moderate amounts'! For a Japanese adult that would be something like one small flask of sáke (rice wine), or a bottle of beer, or two weak whiskey-and-waters. It is also important for those who drink on a daily basis to have a break from doing so one or two days a week to give their liver a rest!

President Ikeda: What about exercise?

Imazeki: Basically, exercise strengthens the heart. The key is determining the proper amount of exercise. If the exercise is too strenuous, it can in fact contribute to heart problems.

Morita: For most people, a brisk thirty-to-forty-minute walk three to five times a week will be sufficient. Those who have ischemic heart disease should confer with their doctor about the proper amount of exercise.

Beware of Sudden Changes in Temperature

President Ikeda: Are there any other areas in our daily lives that we should pay attention to?

For most people, a brisk thirty-to-forty-minute walk three to five times a week will be sufficient. Those who have ischemic heart disease should confer with their doctor about the proper amount of exercise.

Morita: In the winter, one should avoid sudden changes in temperature. When going from a warm place to a cold place, it is always a good idea to put on a coat.

President Ikeda: We have said this before, but it is especially important for the elderly to be careful in cold weather when they go from a heated room into a cold room or go from indoors to outdoors. The former is of particular concern in Japan, where most homes are not centrally heated and rooms, such as the kitchen and bathroom tend to be very cold in winter.

Toyofuku: Also, when bathing, lukewarm baths are preferred. A very hot bath places considerable stress on the heart. One should also get into the bath tub slowly. When using a deep, traditional Japanese-style tube, first just sit up to the waist until your body grows accustomed to the water temperature, then slowly sit down with the water up to your neck.

President Ikeda: It is also a good idea to warm the kitchen and bathroom when you use them during the colder months, isn't it?

Imazeki: Yes. And, remember that the feet tend to get cold quickly, so wear slippers or heavy socks around the house in winter. Some people even put a portable electric heater in the bathroom.

Get Out of Bed Slowly

Morita: Elderly people should be careful when playing with their grandchildren or other young children. Kids have an endless supply of energy, and an older person can get quite tired before he or she knows it. Just lifting a child up puts considerable strain on the heart.

President Ikeda: Earlier, you mentioned that angina and heart attack, both resulting from ischemic disorders, are more likely to occur in the morning. Is there anything we should be careful about when getting out of bed in the morning?

Imazeki: When you are awake, first move your legs and arms gently. Then get up slowly. Never leap out of bed.

TOYOFUKU: You should be careful at night, too. If you happen to be sleeping in a room alone and have a heart attack, no one will find you until morning. People with heart disease should always have a bell or some other warning device at their bedside so that they can let family members know when they are having problems.

IMAZEKI: As mentioned earlier, the worst thing for heart disease is to overexert ourselves in any way. It goes without saying that one should not overeat or drink too much alcohol. It can also be harmful to try to make up for a week's lack of exercise with strenuous activity on the weekend. Skipping breakfast and eating a large lunch and dinner is not wise, either. All of these things put an excessive burden on the heart.

PRESIDENT IKEDA: When you overdo it, you won't be able to go on for very long. Only when you act with moderation and within the bounds of reason can you hope to see lasting benefits or results. But sometimes we overdo it without even being aware of it.

> **When you are tired, it is important to rest. Soka Gakkai 2nd president Josei Toda used to always tell me to do whatever I needed to get sufficient sleep. Getting enough sleep is in itself a crucial challenge in our busy lives.**

TOYOFUKU: Unfortunately, that is true. People who are worried about the condition of their heart should find a means by which they can monitor their health. Knowing your normal pulse, blood pressure, weight and daily amount of sleep can alert you to any irregularities when they occur.

MORITA: Yes, if you are aware of the daily rhythms of your body, then you will be quick to notice any change.

PRESIDENT IKEDA: In a certain sense, each of us must be our own 'doctor' and 'nurse' and watch carefully over our health.

IMAZEKI: People who fear they may have heart problem should be especially careful not to allow themselves to get overtired.

PRESIDENT IKEDA: When you are tired, it is important to rest. Soka Gakkai 2nd president Josei Toda used to always tell me to do whatever I needed to get sufficient sleep. Getting enough sleep is in itself a crucial challenge in our busy lives.

In this period of seasonal change when summer turns to autumn, many people tend to fall ill and many die — not only from heart disease. Life is precious. We have a mission. I hope all of our readers, while praying earnestly for the good health of both their comrades and family members as well as their own, will make a special effort to pilot their lives with wisdom and prudence.

Nursing

Participants in this discussion on
' Humanism and the Art of Medicine:
A New Century of Health'
are SGI President Ikeda, Soka Gakkai
Women's Division Nurses' Group
Leaders Reiko Inamitsu, Kazuko Matsumoto
and Secretary Akiko Kojima

PRESIDENT IKEDA: When we fall ill and go to the hospital, it is invariably the nurses who give us the greatest care and comfort. The presence of a sympathetic nurse can give untold hope and reassurance to a patient. Today, I have the pleasure of talking with representatives from the Women's Division nurses' group (Shirakaba-kai). There are no stern doctors about, so please make yourselves right at home and share your thoughts and feelings freely with our readers.

INAMITSU: Thank you.

MATSUMOTO AND KOJIMA: We will do our best!

PRESIDENT IKEDA: Ms Inamitsu, you are now teaching nursing at a vocational college, aren't you?

INAMITSU: Yes.

PRESIDENT IKEDA: When you were working as a nurse, what departments did you work in?

INAMITSU: I started out in gynaecology (female reproductive system), and later worked in gastroenterology (stomach and intestines), haematology (blood), endocrinology (hormones), ophthalmology (eyes) and a variety of other departments.

PRESIDENT IKEDA: And you, Ms Matsumoto?

MATSUMOTO: I worked in neurology (nervous system) and neurosurgery (brain surgery, etc).

KOJIMA: I worked in infectious diseases and in the gastroenterology ward, where I care for many cancer patients.

PRESIDENT IKEDA: With the three of you, we have an entire hospital's worth of experience!
　　What motivated you to become nurses?

INAMITSU: When I was a junior high school student, I spoke about the founder of the nursing profession as we know it today, Florence Nightingale (1820-

1910), in a local speech contest. As part of my research, I read her biography and was deeply impressed. It was then that I decided to become a nurse.

PRESIDENT IKEDA: I am sure many people have been inspired to become nurses by the example of Florence Nightingale.

MATSUMOTO: Yes, I am personally very fond of her statement that "every woman is a nurse."[1]

PRESIDENT IKEDA: Why did you decide to become a nurse?

MATSUMOTO: I nearly drowned in a pool when I was in the first grade of elementary school. The nurse at the hospital to which I was taken was so kind. I will never forget her comforting me with the simple words, "Everything's going to be all right now." From that time on, I decided that I wanted to be a nurse someday.

KOJIMA: My mother was a nurse. I heard so much about how difficult the job was from her that I decided a nurse was the last thing I wanted to be! But seriously, I did want to learn about taking care of my health, so I enrolled in a nursing school. Then, in my first year there, I became ill and was hospitalised. It was only then that I realised just how important nurses are.

An Unforgettable Nurse

PRESIDENT IKEDA: That was a valuable experience. Actually, only when we have experienced illness ourselves can we really understand the feelings of others who are ill.

I, too, had cause to meet a nurse whom I will never forget. It was during World War II. My four elder brothers had all been drafted into the army and sent to the front. I had to work in a steel factory. I was suffering from a serious case of tuberculosis at the time, but being wartime, any young man who stayed home to convalesce would have been scorned and ridiculed. So, I kept working even though it was really beyond me physically. I also had

---

1. Florence Nightingale, *Notes on Nursing: What it is, and What it is not* (London: Harrison, 1860), pg 5.

to take part in compulsory military training exercises at the factory's 'youth school' [which each sizable Japanese company ran in those days to support the mobilization of all citizens for the war effort ordered by the government].

I was painfully thin, and my cheeks were sunken and drawn. Injections to relieve my condition had little effect; within a short time, my fever would return. On a few occasions, I had to be carried home from work in a rickshaw because I was unable to walk under my own steam. Sometimes, I worked with a fever of 39 degrees Celsius (102.2 degrees Fahrenheit). Obviously, this couldn't continue, and at last, I had no choice but to have the factory transfer me to an office job.

In addition, my family couldn't afford to send me to a doctor for regular medical treatment. Being wartime, there was also a terrible food shortage, so I couldn't get sufficient nourishment. All I could do was to try to take care of my own health to the best of my ability, relying heavily on a magazine, called *Health Adviser*.

It was around this time that an elderly nurse at the factory's health office expressed serious concern about my condition and urged me to go to see a doctor at the hospital. She even accompanied me when I went to the hospital for my x-ray. "You must somehow get a change of air for your lungs," she said. "War is terrible, isn't it? I certainly hope it ends soon." I found her words a great comfort and a source of encouragement.

After the results of my medical examination were known, the hospital

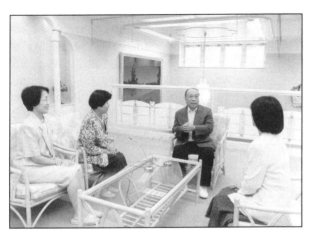

SGI President Ikeda (2nd right), Soka Gakkai Women's Division Nurses' Group Leaders Reiko Inamitsu (2nd left), Kazuko Matsumoto (right) and Secretary Akiko Kojima (left) in discussion.

arranged to send me to a sanatorium for convalescence in the countryside. But very soon after, the war came to an end and any thoughts of hospitalization were then out of .the question.

In any case, I was deeply touched and gladdened by the nurse's kindness to me at that time. The inner strength that enabled her to frankly state her opinion of the war also inspired me with courage and hope. I can still vividly picture her, even now.

INAMITSU: I hope the three of us can someday become the kind of nurses who leave an unforgettable impression on our patients.

PRESIDENT IKEDA: I hope so, too.

Florence Nightingale said, "Nursing is an art."[2] It is the art of health. She said that a painter works with a canvas, and a sculptor, with marble, but a nurse works with the most precious vessel of all, the living body, thus making nursing the finest of fine arts.[3] She was indeed proud of her vocation.

I agree that nursing is an art. A nurse is a healing artist who combines medical expertise, wisdom and character to work her wonders. Nothing could be more admirable. I believe, we must value nurses and the nursing profession more than we do today.

As nurses yourselves, what do you feel to be especially important when it comes to nursing?

Being a Good Listener

MATSUMOTO: First, I think, one must listen carefully to what patients have to say. Having someone listening while they explain their feelings gives patients a chance to get their own thoughts organised; it also makes it easier to clarify any specific worries or problems they may be experiencing.

Let me share an experience I heard from one of our colleagues in the Women's Division nurses' group. Once, among the patients for which she was responsible, there was a man who had just had an operation to have his vocal chords removed. At seventy-three, he was still very active and

---

2. *Memorials of Agnes Elizabeth Jones: by Her Sister*, introduced by Florence Nightingale (London: Strahan and Co, Publishers, 1871), pg 12.
3. Ibid.

involved with the community, where he was well respected and trusted, coaching a children's baseball team and acting as head of his neighbourhood association. The operation had been a success and his throat was healing smoothly, but he clearly grew more and more depressed as the days went by. When our colleague observed this, she prayed that she could learn what was going on in his heart. Then, one day, seeing the patient looking depressed as usual, the nurse went over to say to him, "We're all so worried about you."

The man pulled out a notepad and began scribbling as if his life depended upon it. "I didn't want to have surgery," he wrote. "Nothing good has come of it. I can't go back home. Everyone will laugh at me. I am ashamed to go outside like this." After writing this, he threw the pen down and glowered.

PRESIDENT IKEDA: I see. When he lost his voice, he must have felt as if he had lost everything.

> **By listening to a sick person articulate this inner conflict and pain, we can relieve some of his or her suffering. This accords with the Buddhist teaching of relieving suffering and imparting peace of mind.**

MATSUMOTO: Yes. But the nurse pleaded urgently, "There are so many others here who have had the same surgery. Some of them are still young, and they are all feeling the same pain and frustration as you. I'd like you to encourage them and tell them not to give up. I know, it would really lift their spirits. I can't help feeling that's your mission."

By the time she finished speaking, she thought she saw a more positive light shining in the patient's eyes. From that time on, he completely recovered his former high spirits, and after leaving the hospital he continued to coach the children's baseball team.

PRESIDENT IKEDA: People who are sick always have to deal with inner turmoil of some kind. They carry on a painful inner dialogue with themselves about their illness, posing questions that they then try to answer.

Just by listening to a sick person articulate this inner conflict and pain, we can relieve some of his or her suffering. This accords with the Buddhist teaching of relieving suffering and imparting peace of mind.

And we are not talking about pretending to listen, either. No, we must listen carefully and closely, with true concern. That personal warmth can actually help a person recover from illness.

Expertise and Concern

KOJIMA: Pretence or putting on an appearance of concern certainly has no place in nursing. While professional expertise is naturally important, everything ultimately depends on whether or not, as a nurse, one is really concerned about the patient's well-being. The results can be completely different depending on the nurse's attitude.

INAMITSU: Another member of the nurses' group told me the story of a patient she was caring for who had been in a coma for almost a year. The man's wife came to visit him in the hospital every day. She would talk to him, encourage him and bathe him. The nurse was deeply moved by the wife's devotion.

PRESIDENT IKEDA: What a beautiful example of love between husband and wife!

INAMITSU: Then, one day, a popular song was playing on the television in the room during the wife's visit. The nurse remembered the wife once remarking that her husband liked this kind of song. So, the nurse bent down to the patient, saying, "Let's sing along together." She, too, had come to believe that she could somehow communicate with him even though he was in a coma. She and the wife then began singing along to the music, so that the patient could hear.

A little while later, sounds began to come from the patient's mouth. He was singing. The two women were astonished. They both wept. The nurse thought to herself in wonder at the time, "You've heard your wife's voice all along, haven't you? You've heard it with your life. Her words reached you after all!"

MATSUMOTO: Though such episodes often defy medical explanation, they do happen quite frequently.

After every medical step has been taken, it is the patient's life force that makes them work. And, the support of nursing staff and family members is invaluable in strengthening the patient's life force.

Avoid Depleting the Patient's Life force

PRESIDENT IKEDA: Strengthening the patient's life force is the essence of nursing, isn't it? Florence Nightingale also felt that minimising the expenditure or depletion of the patient's 'vital energy' is of crucial importance in nursing.[4] It is essential to create an environment most conducive to the recovery of each patient, she said, with thought being given to letting in a proper amount of fresh air, making sure the patient gets sufficient sunlight as well as peace and quiet, and maintaining a well-balanced diet and cleanliness.[5]

I feel that Florence Nightingale firmly believed that the key to recovery from illness lies in the patient's life force, or 'vital power', as she called it. The task of nursing is to ensure that the patient's life force is not weakened, and doing whatever possible to strengthen it. The fundamental basis for nursing, therefore, is a deep reverence for life.

MATSUMOTO: We are all striving to become the kind of nurses who can bring comfort just by our presence.

PRESIDENT IKEDA: I hope you will. Because a nurse who makes all quiver with terror will cause an alarming drain on the patients' vital power! Seriously though, cruel and unpleasant nurses are hard for patients to bear.

INAMITSU: The little things are so important, aren't they? Florence Nightingale said, "Nursing is in general made up of little things; little things they are called, but they culminate in matters of life and death."[6]

PRESIDENT IKEDA: Those are very wise words. They are very similar to the attitude that a Buddhist leader must cultivate.

KOJIMA: Once, a patient with a dreadful, itching rash was admitted to a ward where I worked. She was the head nurse of a certain hospital. The itching was so intense that she could not sleep at night. I happened to be on night duty one evening when her symptoms were at their worst. Neither injections

---

4. Florence Nightingale, *Notes on Nursing: What it is, and What it is not* (London: Harrison, 1860), pg 3.
5. Ibid.
6. Florence Nightingale in a message, titled "To the Nurses and Probationers trained under the 'Nightingale Fund,'" London, June 1897.

In nursing, you have to both observe the patients with your eyes and to care for them with your hands.

nor drugs were of any use in relieving her distress.

I didn't know what to do, but I spoke to her soothingly, as I chanted daimoku in my heart. "It itches, doesn't it?" I said. Continuing to offer comforting words, I gently stroked her back and arms. After doing this for about two hours, she finally fell asleep.

INAMITSU: Until morning?

KOJIMA: Yes. She slept soundly. The next morning she thanked me, saying she felt so much better. She added that she had come to realise that what I had done by staying by her side and stroking her back had opened up a whole other side of nursing for her.

PRESIDENT IKEDA: That is a perfect example of what we call the healing touch, isn't it?

INAMITSU: The first Chinese character in the Japanese word for *nursing (kango)* combines the ideographs for 'hand' and 'eye'. In nursing, you have to both observe the patients with your eyes and to care for them with your hands.

Sakyamuni as a Nurse

PRESIDENT IKEDA: I see. Ms Kojima's story reminds me of the fact that Sakyamuni also once gently rubbed a sick person's back to make him well.

KOJIMA: Really?

PRESIDENT IKEDA: There was an ascetic monk who had fallen ill and lived all alone. When Sakyamuni saw how sick he was, he inquired, "Why are you suffering all alone?"

The monk replied, "Being indolent by nature, I have never been able to endure caring for others when they were ill. Consequently, now that I am ill, no one will take care of me."

"I will care for you," Sakyamuni said, and he began gently rubbing the sick monk's body. He continued in this way for some time, and the monk's suffering gradually lessened. Then, Sakyamuni changed the sick man's bedding, bathed him and dressed him in a fresh robe. And finally, when he encouraged the monk to persevere with his practice, the monk's body and mind were filled with joy.

Sakyamuni's hands stroking the body of the sick monk — that, surely, is the healing touch, the symbol of compassion. This story presents the quintessence of nursing, don't you think?

MATSUMOTO: Yes, I do. All of the important elements of nursing — touch, changing bedding, bathing, changing clothes, and offering encouragement — are included in the story.

INAMITSU: There is a profound relationship between Buddhism and nursing, isn't there?

PRESIDENT IKEDA: They are one and the same. Sakyamuni said, "If you would make offerings to me, make offerings to the sick instead."[7] And he also said, "You must make offerings to all sick people with the same reverence that you would make offerings to the Buddha. Nursing the sick is the greatest of all good deeds."[8]

---

7. *Shibun Ritsu* (The Fourfold Rules of Discipline). The *vinaya* or monastic rules of the Dharmagupta School, translated from Sanskrit by Buddhayashas.
8. *Bommo Sutra* (Sutra by Brahma's Net). Translated from Sanskrit into Chinese by Kumarajiva.

Caring for and encouraging the sick are true Buddhist practice and the offering that pleases the Buddha more than any other.

Extending the Spirit of Nursing throughout Society as a Whole

PRESIDENT IKEDA: I don't think that this spirit of nursing should be restricted to professional nurses. There is no one who is a stranger to sickness. Only when society extends the warm spirit of nursing to all will we have a healthy society.

INAMITSU: I think that the spirit of encouragement and the spirit of nursing are alive and well within the SGI.

PRESIDENT IKEDA: I have heard, by the way, that there is a critical shortage of nurses.

KOJIMA: In Japan, some put nursing into those professions regarded as 'dangerous, dirty and difficult'.

MATSUMOTO: Many are calling for reform in the laws regulating the profession.

PRESIDENT IKEDA: I would imagine so.
One problem is that the old image of doctors being superior to nurses has got to go. Rather, aren't doctors and nurses equal partners — colleagues and co-workers, striving together towards a shared goal?

INAMITSU: In one respect, I think you can say that doctors provide the cure and nurses provide the care.

PRESIDENT IKEDA: Nursing is a truly noble profession. We must all recognise the true worth of nurses and their profession.
I am sure nursing is very hard work. But nothing is so wonderful as to be able to care for and to ease the suffering of others. In Buddhism, one who does this is called bodhisattvas. Florence Nightingale declared that it is a privilege to suffer for humanity — "a privilege not reserved to the Redeemer

and the martyrs alone, but one enjoyed by numbers in every age."[9] Nurses are in a position to enjoy this special privilege of saving others.

MATSUMOTO: Regarding nursing as a special privilege reflects a very spiritual state, I think. Why, it makes all one's complaints just fade away!

PRESIDENT IKEDA: Florence Nightingale also said that the kind of person one is, mattered more in nursing than in any other profession.[10] The nursing and the teaching professions rely almost entirely on the quality of the people in them.

INAMITSU: It makes one humble. As members of the SGI and practitioners of Nichiren Daishonin's Buddhism, I think we are very fortunate to be able to develop ourselves through faith and practice.

Visiting the Sick

PRESIDENT IKEDA: What points should we keep in mind when visiting the sick, particularly those in hospital?

INAMITSU: For starters, one should observe the rules of common sense. Only come during visiting hours, and try not to bring children along. It is also important not to have too many people visit at once, not to stay too long, and to be cheerful but not too noisy. All these are important so that you do not disturb other patients or the hospital routine for the patient's treatment.

MATSUMOTO: Rather than encouraging the patient too heartily, it is better to put him or her at ease. Make every effort to give the patient the time he or she needs to recover, without having to worry about mundane matters.

KOJIMA: Never carry on whispered conversations in front of a patient. That only makes him or her think that the visitors are trying to hide something, causing anxiety to the patient. It is also wise to avoid talking about upsetting topics altogether.

---

9. Florence Nightingale, *Cassandra and Other Selections from Suggestions for Thought*, ed Mary Poovey (New York: New York University Press, 1993), pg 209.
10. Florence Nightingale, *Florence Nightingale to Her Nurses* (London: Macmillan and Co, Limited, 1914), pg 5.

INAMITSU: When the patient's family is there, or when there are other patients in the room, it is a nice idea to greet them politely. Remember, if there is any unpleasantness, it is the patient, who remains behind, who will have to deal with it.

PRESIDENT IKEDA: The key point to remember in visiting those who were sick is the same as in nursing — in other words, not to tire the patient, not to deplete their 'vital power'.

I think we can describe nursing as the art of stimulating people's life-force. In that sense, I think that the home is also a suitable place for nursing in the broadest meaning of the term. The home is a place where we can refresh our bodies and minds. It is the place where we feel the safest and most secure.

INAMITSU: That is so true. People tend to think of nursing as something that takes place only in a hospital, or that is directed only at the sick. But nursing is really rooted in our daily lives.

PRESIDENT IKEDA: I think we can look at many household activities — preparing meals and doing laundry, housekeeping, talking with family members — as falling into the category of nursing. After all, it is due to those activities that the members of a family can live healthy lives from day to day. The home is a place where we build and foster health — a place for 'health-creation'.

MATSUMOTO: I guess, in many homes, that makes the mother the head nurse — or no, the head physician!

PRESIDENT IKEDA: In the home, the mother functions as a doctor, pharmacist and nutritionist. She is the chief nurse and the head of a general hospital at the same time. That is why everyone in the family, husband and children alike, should listen to what she says. We should not take a mother's words lightly.

INAMITSU: Our daily habits are extremely important in health. This is especially true for those suffering from diseases, such as diabetes and high blood pressure. In that regard as well, nursing and health maintenance in the home can be very important.

MATSUMOTO: The original meaning of the word *nurse* is to care for and raise children. That means that mothers are the original nurses.

Kojima: My mother was certainly an original then, because she was both a mother and a professional nurse. She was very strict about health matters with us, always making sure we washed our hands and gargled when we came in from outdoors. She was determined to prevent us from getting sick. I am very grateful to my mother for the good health I enjoy today.

Memories of Mother's Concern

President Ikeda: A mother knows more about her family's health than anyone else can. Let me tell you a story about myself when I was a child. One day, I found a package of sweets in the closet and ate it in secret. That night, I awoke with a bad stomach-ache. My mother made me take an old-fashioned home remedy and the pain soon subsided.

She grilled me about what I had eaten, and at first I would not admit what I had done. But she wouldn't let me off the hook! "Everyone else ate what you ate, and no one else has a stomach-ache. Why are you the only one with an upset stomach?" She was tougher than a prosecutor!

It turned out that she had put the sweets in the cupboard quite a long time ago and had completely forgotten all about them.

Also, when I was young, I often had digestive problems, so my mother made me wear a woolen band around my middle to keep my stomach warm. She was very concerned for her family's well-being.

Matsumoto: Mothers are really wonderful, aren't they? They also have a great influence on the health of their family. If they are depressed or irritated, everyone in the family will be affected.

President Ikeda: Even with food, somehow something that has been lovingly prepared by our mothers always tastes so delicious, even if it is just a simple snack. When I was a boy, my mother used to steam a sweet potato for me when I was hungry. It was a time of severe food shortages, and that was quite a delicacy. I still remember the taste of those delicious potatoes.

These days, they say, children have fewer opportunities to eat their mother's home cooking, don't they?

INAMITSU: Many young mothers today serve fast-food or take-out meals when they are too busy to cook. Too much of those foods, however, can lead to nutritional imbalance.

PRESIDENT IKEDA: Mothers are busy, though. I hope that the other members of the family will find ways to help, so that mothers are not exhausted from the many demands placed on them in these hectic, modern times.

MATSUMOTO: Let me share the story of a Mrs K., a member of our nurses' group. Her husband's job forced him to work late and irregular hours. Her two sons, one in senior high school and the other in junior high, returned home from their after-school activities at about seven o'clock. Mrs K., herself often had night nursing duty, so it was difficult to get the whole family together for meals. Her solution was, when she had night duty, to prepare an evening meal in advance that could be easily reheated, and then leave a note. She would write something like: "This is for all three of you. Please do not eat your father's portion." "Even if you do not finish the meat, eat all your vegetables." "Don't forget to brush your teeth."

KOJIMA: Though it may take a little extra effort, such thoughtfulness can be very important, can't they?

MATSUMOTO: One day, when Mrs K., returned from night duty she found that her boys had washed their own dishes. They said they wanted to save her some work. From that time on, they always washed their own dishes when she was on night duty. She also noted that their diet began to become more balanced. It seems they had discovered that leftovers and too much sticky sauce on their food made the dishes harder to wash.

PRESIDENT IKEDA: What a delightful story! It really communicates a warm family atmosphere.

Most mothers are working harder than any of us can imagine. Some suffer from chronic illnesses; some get sick as they grow older. That is why it is so important for all members of the family to watch out for their mother's health and well-being. If she seems at all unwell, it is important to find a reliable doctor or hospital. Family members can also help out by reading up on health and medical matters with their mother and becoming more informed.

INAMITSU: Yes. The most important factor in family health is proper knowledge.

KOJIMA: My mother always used to say that knowledge is our best defence.

PRESIDENT IKEDA: That is true. Now, let me ask you to share some of that knowledge with us. What should every home have to help in health maintenance?

MATSUMOTO: Just basic items, such as a thermometer, a scale, an ice pack, bandages, disinfectant, an antiseptic mouthwash and aspirin or some other pain reliever, are enough, I think.

> **Most mothers are working harder than any of us can imagine. Some suffer from chronic illnesses; some get sick as they grow older. That's why it is so important for all members of the family to watch out for their mother's health and well-being.**

PRESIDENT IKEDA: People should not give injections at home, should they?

KOJIMA: No, an untrained person should not be giving injections. Some patients, of course, such as diabetics, have permission from their doctors to give themselves injections.

Caring for the Sick at Home

PRESIDENT IKEDA: What should we do when there is a sick person in the home?

INAMITSU: Different steps are required depending upon what the illness is and how serious it is. There are a few very widely applicable steps, however. First, place the sick person in the brightest room in the house with the best illumination from outside. If possible, it should be a quiet place, away from the kitchen or the entrance hallway.

It is a good idea to place a bell or some other calling device near the sick person, so he or she can call for help at any time.

KOJIMA: People should be careful not to make late-night telephone calls to a house where there is a sick person.

INAMITSU: Interior lighting should be arranged so that it does not shine directly into the patient's eyes. It is important to keep the temperature and humidity at the most comfortable level for the patient, too. This will vary according to both individual preferences and the nature of the illness.

INAMITSU: For a long convalescence, a bed is more comfortable than Japanese-style futon. But if the patient is sleeping in a futon on the floor, watch out for dampness. The futon and other bedding should be aired daily if possible. Light but warm materials make the best bedding.

MATSUMOTO: Keep the area around the patient clean and neat at all times. When you want to clean up, move the patient to another room. Also, try not to raise too much dust when cleaning.

Good ventilation is also important. Even in winter, open the windows for at least ten minutes morning and evening and let in fresh air. You can do this when you are cleaning the room, so you don't expose the patient to a draft.

Food for the patient should be nutritious and easily digestable. Try to make the meals an enjoyable event. This is especially important for patients who may have dietary restrictions or little appetite. All it takes is a little creativity and imagination.

KOJIMA: If the patient cannot bathe, you should give him or her a hot-water sponge bath daily. This is important both for cleanliness and to improve circulation.

KOJIMA: Also to keep the patient's spirits up and provide them with some diversion, try placing a picture or flowers in the sickroom, or let the patient listen to some music.

INAMITSU: The secret is to think of ways to create a pleasant environment that will assist the patient in recovery.

MATSUMOTO: Is it all right to chant *daimoku* while lying down?

PRESIDENT IKEDA: Of course. Nichiren Daishonin said that when we are sick, we may dispense with the reading of the sutra and just chant Nam-myoho-renge-kyo — there is also no need for us to face the Gohonzon when we do so (cf *WND*, pg 72). As for the amount of *daimoku* or length of time one chants, the important thing is not to be rigid. Judge for yourself what is best for your condition at the time.

We also have to be aware of the patient's emotional and spiritual well-being. People are not machines, after all. A sense of security can make all the difference to their physical condition. What steps can we take to help with this?

KOJIMA: Always greet the patient with a smile. Once when a well-known critic was hospitalised, he put a sign up on the door to his room: "When You Open This Door, Do It With a Smile." After that, all of the nurses, who had fallen into the habit of wearing impassive expressions in the course of their hectic daily routine, smiled as they went into his room. The story passed from wing to wing, until the whole hospital was smiling, I heard. The moral of this story applies not only to hospitals, but to home care as well.

Relieving the Patient's Insecurities and Worries

PRESIDENT IKEDA: That is true. Some patients feel guilty for the trouble and inconvenience their illness is causing others. This can be accentuated when they are recuperating at home. When they are in a hospital, everyone is sick and they feel less 'alone' in their condition, but at home they can feel isolated and anxious.

It is important to put such patients at ease, so they can devote their energies to fighting their illness. How this will be best achieved will vary according to individual needs and character, but there is no denying that a smile from family members is excellent medicine.

MATSUMOTO: A sense of security is very important. When patients go into surgery feeling secure and convinced that they will recover, the anesthetic is more effective and only half as much as the normal amount may be needed to achieve the same effect.

KOJIMA: To provide that sense of security, it is also important to take practical measures to remove any worries from the patient's shoulders. When treatment or convalescence continues for some time, in particular, a patient is likely to be concerned about work or school or appointments with friends. A mother who is ill may worry about the family budget, the housekeeping and her children.

INAMITSU: Though she was not being nursed at home, there was a patient I knew, whom I will call Mrs A., who was worried by just such things. She had surgery for breast cancer and was hospitalised for three weeks. She had three small daughters, the eldest of whom was in the first grade of elementary school.

Her family members told her not to worry, and her own parents were helping out and supporting her, but she remained anxious. She had a whole list of things that kept her worrying — meals, taking the two younger girls to and from kindergarten, making the children's lunches, locating where she kept their changes of clothes, paying the bills and school events.

What did her husband do to ease her mind? He visited her each day in the hospital and made notes of what was worrying her. Then he took care of each thing on the list and reported the outcome to her the next day. He also passed along cards and words of encouragement from relatives and friends. His diligent and considerate care significantly reduced his wife's anxiety.

PRESIDENT IKEDA: We often hear of families that have been strengthened and brought closer together by illness. That is wonderful. On the other hand, there are also cases in which the patient recovers but the family falls apart. That is terrible.

As human beings, we cannot avoid the four sufferings of birth, old age, sickness and death. That is why we should help others when they fall ill, and support each other. Illness is nothing to be ashamed of. What we should be ashamed of is letting our illness get the better of us. This is true of both the individual who is ill and his or her family.

Nichiren Daishonin writes, "Illness gives rise to the resolve to attain the way." (*WND*, pg 937) Many people are first motivated to think about life through the experience of illness. And, many only realise how important their families are, and how precious love and affection is, when they have fallen ill.

Sickness can have other good effects in the family. For example, a family council might be called and jobs assigned to each member. This can help children learn to accept responsibility. A united family gives a sick person a sense of security. And when the family sees the patient is free from worry and anxiety, they, too, feel peace of mind.

Care after Hospitalization

PRESIDENT IKEDA: What sort of things should families bear in mind when caring for a family member who has just been released from the hospital?

INAMITSU: One thing that is important is good communication with the doctor. Let me share the experience of Mrs T., a Women's Division member whose husband had an operation for valvular heart disease. The surgery was a success, and he was able to leave the hospital early. But the doctor warned that the real challenge would be preserving his state of health from then on.

Mrs T. asked the doctor many questions, so that she would know what to do under any circumstances that might arise: how her husband's heart should sound under various conditions, what food she should prepare for him, and how she could reach the doctor in an emergency, for example.

After the operation, her husband's condition changed in various ways, just as the doctor had said it would. Symptoms that the doctor had not warned her of also occurred. Each time something arose, Mrs T. treated it as the doctor instructed. When she could not decide what to do, she would confer with the doctor and make notes of his advice.

Thanks to Mrs T.'s attentive care, her husband not only recovered enough to return to work but stayed on until retirement and then found another job after that.

PRESIDENT IKEDA: Just because you have left the hospital does not mean you are completely recovered.

MATSUMOTO: For some time after leaving the hospital, you are still a patient. You will find yourself in trouble if you think you can just go ahead and do everything you used to do when you enjoyed good health. After surgery, you should not overexert yourself for an entire year, it is said.

INAMITSU: Psychological and emotional recovery from illness are especially important. These are believed to take longer than physical recovery. And the longer one is hospitalised, the longer psychological recovery takes.

KOJIMA: The story of a Mrs H., another nurses' division member, illustrates this point. Mrs H.'s husband was hospitalised with meningitis, and for about a month he remained in a state of semi-consciousness. Finally, his illness was brought under control and after two months he was able to leave the hospital.

After coming home, Mrs H., helped her husband carry out a regimen of walking to restore his strength, taking care not to let him overexert himself. She also nursed him by carefully anticipating his needs with regard to food, clothing and bathing, so that he would not feel disadvantaged.

President Ikeda: She was a nurse by profession, so of course, she would be aware of those needs.

Kojima: Yes. But though his body was recovering, her husband began to express increasing concern as the days went by about his job and his future.

Matsumoto: His psychological recovery could not be brought about by medical knowledge alone.

Kojima: That is right. Mrs H.'s approach was to be even kinder and more encouraging than she had been before. "We live to be eighty nowadays, and you are just forty. You can afford to take some time to recuperate now. We have a long life ahead of us." Other members in the area encouraged him as well.· "You will recover completely; just do not push yourself." "Nothing in life is without a purpose. Consider this a valuable experience." This repeated encouragement from those around him eventually resulted in the husband recovering his spirits, and after a month he had returned successfully to his job.

Encouragement does not mean saying things like, "Get well soon!" Such 'encouragement' can end up putting pressure on the patient who is, after all, the one who is suffering and who wants more than anyone to get well as quickly as possible.

President Ikeda: There is no need to push oneself. And, those around a recovering person should not press or make demands, either. They should patiently watch over him or her, allowing the individual plenty of space and time to get fully well.

Encouragement does not mean saying things like, "Get well soon!"

Such 'encouragement' can end up putting pressure on the patient who is, after all, the one who is suffering and who wants more than anyone to get well as quickly as possible.

People who have never experienced disappointment or setback, people who have up until now obtained everything they wanted, are especially likely to feel such pressure and anxiety when they fall ill. Also, people who are used to giving orders and instructions to others are likely to feel frustrated and impotent when they are ill, and no longer in a position of command, making them vulnerable to depression and loss of self-esteem.

INAMITSU: The human heart is complex, isn't it?

Understanding Others' Feelings

PRESIDENT IKEDA: Then, there are also people who are very stoic and never complain about their own pain or worries. They pretend that everything is all right, telling others, "I'm fine. There's nothing to worry about."

KOJIMA: Such people do take a longer time to recover, it is true. They need someone they can open up to and share their feelings with, instead of suppressing them.

PRESIDENT IKEDA: Yes, that will lead to a quicker recovery.
Those around a sick person should also take care not to meet every expression of concern or worry by the patient with reassuring utterances, such as: "Do not worry!" "Stop fretting." Instead of brushing away the patient's fears with a smile, listen patiently to what he or she has to say. Acknowledge the fears. Say, "Yes, of course you are worried. But we'll pull through this together." This is far more meaningful in terms of encouragement.

MATSUMOTO: Whether in the hospital or at home, it is important for the care givers to understand the patient's feelings.

PRESIDENT IKEDA: Yes. Knowing that one's feelings are recognised and under-stood can be a great source of comfort for someone who is ill. A sick person's feelings are always vacillating. The smallest changes can result in extremes of happiness and sorrow, and a sick person's thoughts generally tend to be pessimistic. Little things that wouldn't bother a healthy person can really disturb someone who is sick. Perhaps only someone who has experienced illness can understand.
Florence Nightingale once said in an address to her nurses that the nerves of the sick are always in the state that theirs, the nurses', were in after staying up all night working.[11]

---

11. Florence Nightingale, *Notes on Nursing: What It is and What It is Not* (London: Harrison, 1860), pg 88.

MATSUMOTO: That is so true. I have heard of people so bothered by a spot on the ceiling that they couldn't sleep.

KOJIMA: Little things like the height of one's pillow or the way the sheets are tucked in can bother a sick person so much that they delay recovery.

INAMITSU: Patients can be very stressed by their illness, so we must try to do whatever we can to respond to their requests and make them feel more comfortable. When children are ill, it is important to be especially sweet to them.

PRESIDENT IKEDA: First, do not add to the patient's anxieties. Second, if at all possible, try to relieve those anxieties. Finally, give peace of mind and hope. These are the ways we strengthen the life-force of those who are battling illness.

PRESIDENT IKEDA: We are currently seeing a rapid greying of Japanese society.

MATSUMOTO: Yes. In the 21st century, Japan will have one of the world's largest populations of senior citizens.

PRESIDENT IKEDA: According to some estimates, by the year 2020, one in four Japanese citizens will be over the age of sixty-five. A well-known philosopher has said that ageing gracefully is more difficult than dying. In this age of rising longevity, how we spend our old age is becoming an increasingly important subject of concern. Let us consider this issue today from the perspective of nursing care for the elderly.

Physical Changes that Go Unnoticed

PRESIDENT IKEDA: First, what points should we pay special attention to when caring for the health of the elderly?

KOJIMA: The most important thing is not to let elderly patients overexert themselves. As one ages, overall body strength and muscle tone decline, and various bodily functions also deteriorate.

INAMITSU: We must be careful not to overlook changes in the elderly person's general condition. As people age, they often fail to notice changes in their own physical condition or overall health. As a nurse, I have often found elderly people who were looking somewhat less energetic than usual to be actually running a fever. Then, again, there are others who may be ill but not necessarily having a fever. So, we have to be alert for other signs of illness, such as a loss of appetite or a swelling of the arms or legs.

KOJIMA: When nursing the elderly, bath time is a good opportunity for an 'instant check-up'. Any surface problems will quickly come to light. For instance, they could have a rash without knowing it and which, if it remains untreated, could become infected.

INAMITSU: Other warning signs are frequent visits to the toilet, chronic constipation, a disinclination to leave the house, or withdrawal and silence. All these symptoms can be the first indications of illness.

MATSUMOTO: We need to pay special attention in cases where the elderly have chronic illnesses, such as diabetes or high blood pressure, and make sure they receive treatment while their symptoms are still relatively mild.

Avoiding Falls in the Home

PRESIDENT IKEDA: We often hear of the elderly falling and hurting themselves, and they frequently have accidents at home. With age, our sense of balance deteriorates, as has been indicated in balancing experiments where people are told to stand on one leg.

MATSUMOTO: Yes. Steps or differences in floor level are a major cause of falls. It is best to reduce the height of steps inside the house as much as possible, or replace them with ramps where possible.

KOJIMA: It is also important to keep the floor clear. Do not leave electric cords stretching across the room, or piles of newspapers and magazines lying about. They are easy to trip over. Bright interior lighting helps. The floor area should also be well lit so that the elderly persons can see where they are walking. And, it is a good idea to put non-slip tape along the edges of any stairs to prevent accidental slips and falls.

Matsumoto: Clothing should also be comfortable and easy to move in. Slippers usually lack tread, so extra care should be taken when wearing them to prevent slipping. When going outside, well-fitting canvas shoes are the safest.

Inamitsu: When going shopping, it is a good idea for the elderly to use a small back-pack to carry their purchases. It leaves both hands free, aiding good balance and allowing them to catch themselves should they trip.

Matsumoto: But in spite of all these efforts and precautions, in some cases, elderly people become unable to take care of themselves due to illness or injury from some accident. That is when full-fledged nursing care becomes necessary.

It is important to keep the floor clear. Do not leave electric cords stretching across the room, or piles of newspapers and magazines lying about. They are easy to trip over. Bright interior lighting helps. The floor area should also be well lit so that the elderly persons can see where they are walking. And, it is a good idea to put non-slip tape along the edges of any stairs to prevent accidental slips and falls.

Hygiene, Diet and Elimination

President Ikeda: What are the important points in daily nursing care?

Inamitsu: Hygiene, diet and elimination. Keeping the body clean not only prevents infections and other diseases but makes the patient feel better physically and mentally.

Kojima: Wait until the elderly patient is feeling well enough to be bathed. Two baths a week are about right. The water should be tepid, not hot, and it is a good idea to splash a little on the patient's hands and feet before placing them in the tub. They should stay in the bath for not more than fifteen minutes. They should then be dried thoroughly immediately after the bath to prevent them catching a chill.

INAMITSU: For an elderly person in frail physical health, taking a bath can be as strenuous as mountain climbing. That is why it is a good idea to keep up a conversation with the patient throughout the bath, to make sure things are going well and that they are all right.

MATSUMOTO: Bathing an elderly person requires considerable strength. Slips and falls can occur easily in the bath, and it is usually best to have another person to assist you. You can wrap a towel around the patient's waist in order to suppport them safely as you try to move them.

PRESIDENT IKEDA: What can be done when an elderly patient is not well or strong enough to have a full-fledged bath?

INAMITSU: In such cases, give the patient a sponge bath in bed. Wipe the patient's entire body with a warm, damp towel, using firm but gentle strokes. This will have a massaging function as well, and help prevent bedsores.

KOJIMA: A good sponge bath is hard work. Both the nurse and the patient can be easily tired by such a bath, so it is often advisable to split the process over two days, doing the upper body one day and the lower body the next, for example.

MATSUMOTO: You can also wash a patient's hair in bed. Even just massaging the patient's scalp with a warm, damp towel or alcohol, and then wiping it dry cleanses and refreshes. Every patient should have their hair washed or cleansed once a week.

KOJIMA: Cleanliness raises a patient's spirits. When they have had their hair washed, we often see female patients suddenly brighten up and say, "I wonder if I will have a visitor today."

INAMITSU: It is easy to wash the hands and feet in bed. Place warm water in a deep basin and let the hands or feet soak. A foot-bath can warm the entire body on a cold night and help the patient sleep peacefully.

Food Caught in the Windpipe can Cause Pneumonia

PRESIDENT IKEDA: What should we pay attention to as far as diet is concerned?

INAMITSU: Low-calorie meals with plenty of variety are best. Fat and salt can lead to obesity and high blood pressure. Elderly people can be susceptible to constipation, so we should make sure they consume sufficient fibre in the form of vegetables. Drinking plenty of water will prevent dehydration and additional calcium can reduce the danger of broken bones.

KOJIMA: With age, it becomes more difficult to chew and swallow. This can lead, especially in bedridden patients, to food or saliva entering the windpipe, which can cause pneumonia. Even bedridden patients should sit up in bed, whenever possible, at meal times.

MATSUMOTO: We should also try to make it possible for the elderly patient to eat what the rest of the family eats. All it takes is a little thought in cooking technique. Foods that are grilled, fried or stir-fried generally require a lot of chewing, whereas simmering, boiling and steaming make foods softer and therefore easier for the elderly to eat. Slicing meat and vegetables into small pieces or scoring them also makes them easier to chew.

INAMITSU: Crumbly or powdery foods can get easily caught in the throat or go down the wrong way, so care should be taken with them as well.

PRESIDENT IKEDA: We often hear of elderly people choking on Japanese rice cakes.

MATSUMOTO: Yes. Freshly pounded rice cakes, in particular, are sticky and must be eaten carefully. Rice cakes are easier to eat when they are cut up into small, bite-sized pieces.

KOJIMA: Care should also be taken even with ordinary foods. When one tries to speak with food in one's mouth, for example, the food can get stuck in the throat.

Preserving the Dignity of the Elderly

PRESIDENT IKEDA: Taking care of an elderly patient's elimination needs can be quite a task.

When caring for an elderly person, then, it is important to take their feelings of embarrassment into consideration.

INAMITSU: Elimination is the most private of human activities, and it involves a person's sense of dignity. Elderly patients tend to avoid asking for help in this area because they do not want to cause trouble to others. Most try as much as possible to go to the bathroom on their own.

PRESIDENT IKEDA: When caring for an elderly person, then, it is important to take their feelings of embarrassment into consideration.

MATSUMOTO: Yes. But as hard as we try to do this, there are people who prefer to go about their elimination unaided. If possible, the family might consider installing a handrail in the bathroom. If they have a Japanese-style toilet, they can attach a seat to it so the elderly person does not have to squat. Every effort should be made to facilitate ease and comfort.

KOJIMA: When the patient cannot get to the bathroom unaided, it is generally a good idea to prepare a portable toilet. Even for patients who can walk, a night time trip to the toilet in the dark can be dangerous, and in many Japanese homes the toilet is a cold room. A portable toilet is a safer alternative.

INAMITSU: If the patient tends to suffer from constipation, it can be effective to massage the area around the navel gently in a circular motion.

Regular Visits to the Toilet

KOJIMA: When a patient is incontinent, it is a good idea to start with a hospital check-up. There is always the possibility that the incontinence has been caused by an illness. When illness is not the cause, incontinence can often be controlled by teaching the patient to visit the toilet regularly.

INAMITSU: Yes, it can be most helpful for the person to get into the habit of going to the toilet at regular intervals, even when they do not feel the desire to urinate.

PRESIDENT IKEDA: In other words, one shouldn't immediately put elderly patients in diapers.

INAMITSU: That is right. Many find that embarrassing, and the best strategy is to make efforts to avoid incontinence from the beginning. But there are times when the patient does not make it to the toilet in time. Believe me, no one feels worse than the patient about such accidents. Censuring the patient creates no value.

MATSUMOTO: One of the important points of nursing the elderly is not damaging their self-esteem. One should not talk down to them, as if they were children or inferiors. Speak to them just as you did before they fell ill.

KOJIMA: The various problems and limitations that occur with ageing are difficult for the patient to accept. Most elderly people are very much aware that they cannot do many things as they once did.

PRESIDENT IKEDA: That is why it is so important to respect their dignity. After all, it was in long years of service to their family and society that they grew old. Now that they need help, it is the perfect opportunity for us to repay our gratitude for their efforts.

Nothing robs the elderly of their energy and spirit so much as loneliness. And, nothing cheers them up more than the love of their friends and family, strong social ties and pleasant conversation.

The Bedridden can Walk Again

INAMITSU: That is very true. I heard the following story from a Ms K., a visiting nurse who cares for the sick at home. Ms K. was assigned as the visiting nurse of a Mrs H., who had been bedridden for twenty years. When Ms K. first visited her new patient's home, she was astonished. The storm shutters to her room were drawn, leaving it in total darkness, and there was a bedpan left at her pillow. Mrs H. was living with her children and grand-children, but their lives were separate, and they rarely even spoke to each other.

KOJIMA: They had given up on her, assuming that once bedridden she would never get well and that it would be impossible for them to live together as a family.

INAMITSU: Ms K. began by trying to change these notions of Mrs H.'s family. She had them open the sliding storm shutters to let in fresh air and light, and air her bedding. And, to help Mrs H. distinguish between day and night, Ms K. had her wear a white apron over her pajamas during the day.

Ms K. told the family to make special efforts to talk to Mrs H., even just to say little things, such as "Good morning," "Good night," "How are you feeling?" "Today's weather is beautiful, so let's open the window," or "I hope you can eat with us at the dining table soon."

Through this interaction with her family, Mrs H. began to think, "I cannot just stay in bed all day. I will try to get up." She began to practise crawling around her room, challenging herself a little more each day, and steadily regained her strength.

She had been bedridden for twenty years, so of course at times she would be tired, frustrated, and about to give up, but her family encouraged and helped her. Six months later, Mrs H. could finally walk with the aid of a cane. She was also able to eat with the family. Mrs H. expressed her gratitude to them: "I never thought food could taste this good. Thank you!"

PRESIDENT IKEDA: What a wonderful story! A bedridden person can become active again.

KOJIMA: Yes. The majority of bedridden patients can get up and walk again with proper nursing care and encouragement to be self-reliant and independent. I think it is important when nursing the bedridden to have that as a goal.

The Bodily Functions Deteriorate in the Bedridden

PRESIDENT IKEDA: Why is it that people become bedridden?

KOJIMA: Most patients become bedridden when a stroke or nerve damage makes it impossible to move their bodies freely. You will also often find that elderly patients become bedridden as a consequence of initially being confined to bed with a cold or a broken bone.

MATSUMOTO: It is said that in just one day in bed, the body's muscular strength drops by three per cent. When one is confined to bed for a long period of time, the joints become stiff and muscle tissue shrinks. Heart and lung function also starts to deteriorate. As a result, it becomes difficult to get out of bed. Often the patient becomes depressed and loses the will to recover. This can also lead to becoming bedridden.

INAMITSU: We nurses have a saying: "Confine a patient to bed and they will stay bedridden." Too much nursing care can cause a patient to lose their independence and self-sufficiency. This leads to a gradual loss of many abilities, until the person no longer attempts to do even things that they ought to be able to manage quite easily for themselves.

Sitting is the Best Way to Prevent One Becoming Bedridden

PRESIDENT IKEDA: What are some steps we can take to prevent elderly patients from becoming bedridden?

MATSUMOTO: Sitting up is the first step out of bed. Instead of allowing the patient to give up because they cannot walk, they should be encouraged to sit up when eating and watching television. Sitting up will also help prevent bedsores.

INAMITSU: When half of the body is paralysed, it can become difficult to support oneself while sitting, so a back support is necessary. A bed chair can be used, or a quilt can be folded and placed behind the back as a support.

KOJIMA: A wheelchair, if available, can also be quite helpful in getting the patient out of bed for a period of time. The patient can then watch television and eat with the family in the same room. If a wheelchair is not available, a chair with back support can be provided, and the patient moved there from time to time.

Encourage but Do Not Help

MATSUMOTO: As we mentioned earlier, one of the key points in nursing bedridden patients is to encourage them to do whatever they can for themselves.

KOJIMA: Even those with some disability or who are very elderly should be encouraged to take care of themselves to the best of their ability. The nurse or family members should only help out with what the patient really cannot manage to do.

The basic idea is "encourage but don't help." I think it is especially productive to encourage elderly patients to take care of their own personal needs, such as eating and dressing.

INAMITSU: Nurses and families often think only of their own convenience. They do things for the patient because it takes more time or it is more trouble if they let the patient do it themselves. This may seem to be kindness at first glance, but in fact, it is the coldest way to treat a patient.

MATSUMOTO: Elderly people who are not bedridden, but still relatively healthy, should be encouraged to help with simple tasks around the home, like taking the washing off the clothes-line, cleaning the entrance hallway, or putting away the dishes. This gives them some light exercise and also the feeling that they are contributing to the family.

PRESIDENT IKEDA: It gives them a purpose. One of our challenges as human beings is how we maintain a sense of purpose each day. The important thing is to continually strive to find something that gives one joy and hope, and thereby bring one's life to a fulfilling and satisfying completion. In any effort, it is the finishing stages that are very important. Similarly, the final chapter of our life is crucial.

Even though one is ill — in fact, precisely when one is ill — one can experience a rich spiritual life. A person who is spiritually fulfilled remains clear of mind and heart even though their body may be ailing, and gains a deep understanding of many aspects of life.

Preventing Bedsores

PRESIDENT IKEDA: Are bedsores the most difficult problem in nursing the bedridden?

MATSUMOTO: Yes. When one is in bed for a long time, in the same position, the circulation of blood to the parts of the body in contact with the bed is reduced, and bedsores result. Vitamin deficiencies or insufficient protein in the diet can also cause bedsores.

PRESIDENT IKEDA: Where do bedsores most frequently occur?

MATSUMOTO: On the back of the head, the shoulders, the elbows, the back, below the hip bones, on the buttocks, ankle and heel.

One of our challenges as human beings is how we maintain a sense of purpose each day. The important thing is to continually strive to find something that gives one joy and hope, and thereby bring one's life to a fulfilling and satisfying completion.

Patients should be Turned in Bed Every Two Hours

PRESIDENT IKEDA: How can they be prevented?

KOJIMA: By turning the patients in bed every two hours. For example, from lying on their back, turn them to lie on their right side, then on their back again, and then on their left side, and repeat.

PRESIDENT IKEDA: Must they be turned every two hours even at night?

KOJIMA: Ideally, yes, but that is very difficult for those who are caring for the patient to do. It is also helpful to thoroughly massage the places bedsores frequently occur before putting the patient to sleep, and cushioning those areas with something soft.

INAMITSU: It is also important to keep the skin dry, so if the patient is wearing diapers, they should be changed promptly whenever they are wet.

Bathing is Effective

PRESIDENT IKEDA: What can be done to treat bedsores?

MATSUMOTO: Many think that a patient with bedsores should not bathe, but in fact the opposite is true. Bathing cleans the sores and warms the body, hastening healing. It is important, however, to thoroughly dry the areas after the bath and apply antiseptics and salves. Once a bedsore has appeared in a certain area, it is likely to re-occur, so it would not do to be careless.

PRESIDENT IKEDA: My father-in-law lived to be eighty-five. He was ill the last three years of his life, and he was bedridden in the final year. My mother-in-law continued to nurse him very diligently. My father-in-law was a large man, and my mother-in-law's back became bent from her constant exertions to move him. But as a result of her efforts, he never suffered from bedsores.

INAMITSU: We nurses say that bedsores are a sign of bad nursing. The proof of truly devoted nursing at a hospital is the absence of bedsores among its patients. But no matter how dutifully one turns the patients, some come down with bedsores because they are in poor general physical health. When bedsores are detected, the first thing to do is to have a doctor examine the patient.

PRESIDENT IKEDA: My mother-in-law always read to her husband, from the *Seikyo Shimbun* and other newspapers. That way he kept up on the news and what was happening in the world. From what I observed, neither husband nor wife — patient nor the 'care-giver' — appeared sad or be hard done by.

Their son, daughter-in-law and grandchildren lived with them and supported my mother-in-law in her efforts. Though my father-in-law was bedridden, the family actually became more cheerful and harmonious through caring for him.

The cooperation of all family members is vital in nursing the elderly, isn't it?

INAMITSU: It certainly is. In Japan, nursing the elderly at home usually places an especially heavy burden on the person's daughter or daughter-in-law. But it should not be that way. One person should not be responsible for all the nursing care. Each family member should think about what they can do to help, and specific tasks should be assigned to each of them, dividing the work.

PRESIDENT IKEDA: You are right. That will also cultivate a spirit of compassion among the care-givers in the family, including the children, if there are any. And, that is a very important thing.

KOJIMA: I am reminded of the experience of a Mr A. His mother had a spinal problem and was paralysed from the chest down. She required twenty-four-hour nursing care, and most of the burden fell on Mr A.'s wife.

While Mr A. continually felt indebted to his wife and sorry that she had so much to do, his own work kept him very busy, and he really did not help out as much as he should have. Lifting and caring for Mr A.'s mother, who was completely immobile, was heavy labour. Eventually, Mrs A. hurt her own back. Her mother-in-law felt so remorseful when that happened. From that time on, she was continually apologising, repeating, "It is my fault, it is my fault."

Concerned that unless the situation changed, everyone in the family would suffer, Mr and Mrs A. had a talk and decided that Mr A. would be responsible in caring for his mother at night. Mr A.'s sister also began to come twice a week to help out. And, the couple's two children — one in junior high and one in elementary school — also pitched in to help, asking their grandmother if she had anything she would like them to do for her.

Help the Care-giver with Words and Actions

PRESIDENT IKEDA: I hope everyone will be considerate of the care-giver. Usually, this turns out to be the patient's daughter or daughter-in-law, who in many cases is also a busy wife and mother. We must not take them and all the work they do around the home for granted.

It is particularly important for husbands to understand what their wives go through. Too many men seem to think that they do not have to concern themselves with the way the household runs.

And we should also remember that no matter how grateful we may be in our hearts, the other person does not know it unless we speak up. It is so easy just to say, "Thank you," or "We really appreciate you," offering words of heart-felt appreciation and encouragement.

Those who are being nursed should also remember to say, "Thank you," to the family members who are helping them.

MATSUMOTO: Other family members not living in the same house as the elderly patient shouldn't leave everything up to those who are. They should come to help on a regular basis, giving those who are doing the nursing on a day-to-day basis a much-needed chance to rest.

PRESIDENT IKEDA: And, it is no good if visiting relatives allow themselves to be treated like guests. They should be there to help, not to sit in the living room and make those who need their help serve them. The important thing is to give those who perform the daily nursing care a rest. Those around them should also ensure these daily care-givers get enough rest everyday.

Use Public Services

INAMITSU: When a family takes the entire nursing task upon itself, its members can have a difficult time attending local events or going out as a family. And, no doubt they will also have questions about proper nursing care. In both cases, they should make use of public nursing services that are available.

PRESIDENT IKEDA: What kind of services are there?

KOJIMA: There are services that offer necessary equipment, such as portable toilets and beds; bathing services; 'day care' services that bring the patient to a facility and teach them things, such as daily life skills; 'short stay' services, which will care for the elderly patient on a temporary, short-term basis; 'home help' services, which give advice on nursing care and also offer assistance in preparing meals and feeding, and in helping patients go to the bathroom and bathing.

MATSUMOTO: These services are provided by local autonomous bodies and the fees vary from area to area. It is a good idea to confer first with a doctor specialising in care of the elderly, a social worker, the Health and Welfare Ministry's consultation services for the elderly, or one's local social welfare office.

PRESIDENT IKEDA: Of course, the feeling of responsibility to care for one's own parents by oneself is important, but there is also much to be said for using the available social services.

INAMITSU: I think so. Compared to many Western nations, Japanese families bear more of the burden in the care of their elderly.

We are seeing increasing numbers of our nurses' group (Shirakaba-kai) members establishing their own visiting-nurse services. Through those services, they are actively helping with the nursing of mainly the elderly and also providing advice on nursing care.

KOJIMA: Care for the elderly cannot continue solely within the confines of the family. We must employ broader social networks.

MATSUMOTO: Today, there are some two million people who need nursing care in Japan. By 2025, when the elderly population is expected to peak, that number will have risen to an estimated 5.2 million.

Building a Culture that Values the Elderly

PRESIDENT IKEDA: It is certainly a major problem, but I do not think we should view it only with pessimism. Instead, I think it is important for society as a whole to use it as an opportunity to foster a culture that values the elderly. A culture that values the elderly is a culture that values humanity.

We need to make efforts in both the family and society at large to create such a compassionate and spiritually rich culture, and at the same time build practical networks to meet the needs of the elderly.

Youth and the aged each have their fine qualities. The long years of experience that the elderly can offer are an invaluable asset for society. And, as the Greek dramatist, Sophocles (496-406 BC), once said, "Nobody loves life like the old." Our society is definitely ageing; I hope we can transform it into a society filled with love for humanity and wisdom about life.

Senile Dementia

Participants in this discussion on
' Humanism and the Art of Medicine:
A New Century of Health'
are SGI President Ikeda, Soka Gakkai
Women's Division Nurses' Group
Leaders Reiko Inamitsu, Kazuko Matsumoto
and Secretary Akiko Kojima

President Ikeda: Our topic for today is senile dementia[1]. In conversation, people frequently say that people who are very forgetful are 'senile'. How is that different from real senility, or senile dementia?

Inamitsu: Forgetfulness is one of the manifestations of ageing. To a certain extent, it is unavoidable, just like wrinkles. In contrast, senile dementia is a degenerative disease that occurs mainly in the brain.

Matsumoto: Benign forgetfulness is characterised by forgetting simply a certain part of an experience. With dementia, however, one forgets the entire experience and, in addition, one has no awareness even that one has forgotten anything.

President Ikeda: The difference, I guess, we could say very simply then, is that an elderly person who remembers that he ate breakfast but forgot what he had to eat is merely suffering from a decline in memory function, but that an elderly person who forgets that he has eaten breakfast altogether has symptoms of senile dementia.

Kojima: Yes, that is the distinction. Dementia makes it difficult to live a normal life. If left untreated, the forgetfulness becomes even worse.

Alzheimer's Disease and Multi-infarct Dementias

President Ikeda: Alzheimer's disease[2] is a well-known form of senile dementia.

Inamitsu: Yes. The most common types of senile dementia are those caused by Alzheimer's disease and multi-infarct dementias[3], the latter being caused by stroke and other vascular disorders.

---

1. Senile dementia: A progressive degenerative disease of the brain, the most common causes of which are Alzheimer's disease and multi-infarct dementia caused by high blood pressure or some other vascular condition, such as cerebral arteriosclerosis.
2. Alzheimer's disease: A degenerative brain disease characterised by the death of nerve cells in the cerebral cortex, causing atrophy in frontal and temporal lobes. It is the largest single cause of senile dementia.
3. Multi-infarct dementias: Also known as vascular dementias. Caused by a serious impairment to the brain's cognitive functions due to arteriosclerosis-induced cerebovascular disease.

MATSUMOTO: Alzheimer's accounts for more than half the cases of senile dementia worldwide. The disease leads to changes in the brain cells themselves, but the cause is still unknown.

KOJIMA: In multi-infarct dementias, in contrast, blood vessels supplying the brain become blocked and impair the brain's function.

PRESIDENT IKEDA: Is Alzheimer's named after the doctor who discovered it?

MATSUMOTO: Yes, it is. Dr Alois Alzheimer, a German neuropathologist active in the early years of this century, first published a paper on the disorder in 1907.

The Symptoms of Dementia can be Ameliorated

PRESIDENT IKEDA: Can benign forgetfulness caused as a result of old age be treated?

INAMITSU: If active measures are taken, the condition can be improved in most cases.

PRESIDENT IKEDA: How about senile dementia? Can it be cured?

MATSUMOTO: In some cases, early treatment can lead to recovery. But unfortunately, at present there is no known cure for either Alzheimer's disease or multi-infarct dementias.

INAMITSU: But proper nursing can alleviate some of the more obvious symptoms and slow the progress of the disease. This, in turn, can result in a greatly reduced nursing load. Therefore, it is really important to begin appropriate treatment and nursing at the earliest stage possible.

PRESIDENT IKEDA: Does it sometimes happen that senile dementia occurs simultaneously with a decline in memory function that is the result of ordinary ageing?

KOJIMA: Yes. They are actually interrelated in a very complex way. Thus, though we may not be able to cure senile dementia at this point, by

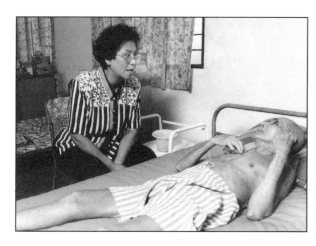

Proper nursing can alleviate some of the more obvious symptoms and slow the progress of senile dementia.

lessening the severity of the symptoms of reduced mental function that is merely the result of ageing, the condition of those suffering from dementia can be significantly improved.

PRESIDENT IKEDA: That means to say that what we have learnt about how to approach and deal with dementia will also be of use in preventing and treating ordinary mental deterioration. Let us start by looking at the symptoms of senile dementia. What are they?

MATSUMOTO: Severe loss of memory function is perhaps most characteristic — especially forgetting where one has put away the things. Often the person can no longer perform simple calculations or mental arithmetic.

INAMITSU: Another common symptom is repeating oneself, or asking the same question again and again. The person begins to forget the names of people and things, and as a result the frequency of expressions, such as "What's-his-name," "You know, that thing . . . What's it called?" starts to increase.

KOJIMA: Another symptom is a loss of interest in things that were once important to the person, like favourite television programme or hobbies.

INAMITSU: When you notice any of these symptoms, and significant changes in speech or behavioural patterns, you should encourage them to go and see a doctor without delay.

PRESIDENT IKEDA: In such cases, I do not imagine people would take kindly to being told, "I think you have senile dementia. You should really see a doctor."

KOJIMA: Yes, that is one of the problems. Very few elderly patients in the first stages of senile dementia are aware that anything's wrong with them. They are certain they are not sick. Others bristle when someone tells them what to do; if you tell them that they need to see a doctor, they will refuse.

MATSUMOTO: In such cases, try to persuade the person to get a general check-up, or have their usual doctor or someone they will listen to urge them to have a medical examination.

PRESIDENT IKEDA: I see. We must use our wisdom. For wisdom is also an expression of love. It would be wonderful if we could all view ageing and senility as the noble price an individual has paid for working hard all their life for the sake of others, their family and society, and give earnest thought to how we can make things easier and more comfortable for them.

If Senile Dementia is Diagnosed

PRESIDENT IKEDA: What kind of things do we need to pay attention to when someone in our family is diagnosed with senile dementia?

KOJIMA: First, look after them carefully so that they remain physically healthy and don't fall ill from some other disease.

MATSUMOTO: The person's ability to concentrate will deteriorate, so special care must be taken to prevent household accidents, particularly falls. Drugs and other dangerous substances should be kept carefully out of reach.

INAMITSU: Another point to consider is to avoid making sudden changes in the person's surroundings or daily routine. A change in the arrangement of a room, for example, can confuse them and exacerbate symptoms of disorientation. Nor should we alter their lifestyle drastically from the way it was before the onset of dementia. Depriving them of the chance to take care of themselves, for instance, can hasten their mental deterioration.

KOJIMA: We should encourage them to take care of themselves as much as they possibly can. Only help them with the things that they cannot do on their own.

MATSUMOTO: Try to preserve a normal daily rhythm in the patient's life. Make a clear distinction between day and night, periods of activity and periods of rest. The elderly often lose the natural rhythms of sleep and drowse during the day. Then they can't sleep at night, and a vicious circle is set in motion.

KOJIMA: It is important to make sure that they are dressed in clean clothes at all times. Unless we take care to change their clothes frequently, they will not only get used to being dirty but their daily habits in general will become slovenly, and that, in turn, has a major effect on their mental and emotional state.

INAMITSU: If the person's symptoms are still mild, insisting that they eat properly, walk properly and greet others in a normal fashion will help contribute to their mental alertness.

Speak in Clear, Short, Simple Phrases

PRESIDENT IKEDA: We should also pay attention to the way we communicate and interact with those suffering from senile dementia, shouldn't we?

INAMITSU: Yes. Start with the way you speak. Those with dementia have reduced memory and comprehension abilities, so speak to them in clear, short, simple phrases.

MATSUMOTO: Restrict each sentence to one topic. For example, instead of saying, "Let us take a bath, then change our clothes, then eat," parcel out the information. First, "Let us take a bath." After the bath, you can say, "Let us change our clothes." When that is finished, it is time to say, "Let us eat."

KOJIMA: And speak slowly, so the person can easily comprehend you.

PRESIDENT IKEDA: Some people lose the power of speech as their disease progresses.

INAMITSU: Yes. When that happens, one can hold the person's hand, or sit or walk close beside them, and communicate through touch or gesture. With some people, you can communicate in writing, or through pictures.

Though Mental Abilities Decline, Emotional Life Persists Unchanged

PRESIDENT IKEDA: What else should we be aware of?

MATSUMOTO: A person with senile dementia may say and do things that are difficult to understand. Nevertheless, it is important not to panic, not to get angry, and to always treat them with kindness and a smile.

KOJIMA: The forgetfulness and other things a senile person might do are not done on purpose. Remember, the person is suffering from a disease and cannot help what is happening to them.

PRESIDENT IKEDA: In other words, we must not scold or reproach them as if it were their fault.

INAMITSU: Precisely. We must also remember that in most cases the loss of memory and other mental capabilities is not accompanied by a loss of feeling or sense of personal dignity. Because of that, the patient is very sensitive to the emotions of those nursing them.

MATSUMOTO: It is a terrible mistake to think that someone who is senile does not understand what you say, or will forget it soon, so you can say whatever you like. Though the exact content of what you said may soon be forgotten, your critical tone of voice will be long remembered.

PRESIDENT IKEDA: People with senile dementia still have feelings. So, instead of arguing or trying to reason with them, we should be considerate of how they feel.

INAMITSU: Yes. We say that in nursing those with dementia, it is better to go along with them than argue with them. Instead of trying to make patients understand what we want, we make an effort to understand what they want, and work from there.

PRESIDENT IKEDA: Yes. Although I am sure that is much easier said than done, it is still extremely important to make such efforts. Those suffering from senile dementia are doing their best, afflicted as they are with a debilitating disease. There is very often some kind of reason or source for their different symptoms, such as anxiety or loneliness, or some personal trauma or emotion they have long endured or suppressed. There is an unheard inner cry seeking release. I think that good nursing care starts with a desire to understand what is disturbing the patient and to heal their pain.

Unlike other types of nursing, I am sure that caring for those with senile dementia can be disheartening at times. However devotedly one cares for such patients, often they cannot express either gratitude or understanding. But the mind is truly mysterious. On the most profound level of life, the patient often really does understand, even though they may not appear to.

> **Caring for those with senile dementia can be disheartening at times. However devotedly one cares for such patients, often they cannot express either gratitude or understanding. But the mind is truly mysterious. On the most profound level of life, the patient often really does understand, even though they may not appear to.**

'My Wife's Senility Changed My Life'

KOJIMA: That reminds me of a story that appeared once in the *Seikyo Shimbun* (October 3, 1990), recounting a Mr H.'s experience in caring for his wife who had senile dementia. Mr H. first noticed that something was amiss with his wife when he himself was hospitalised. She tried to straighten up the things on his bedside table, and after an hour still did not finish. Not only that, but she could no longer find her way home.

INAMITSU: In other words, Mrs H. was showing signs of senile dementia.

KOJIMA: That is right. An examination at the hospital revealed that she was suffering from multi-infarct dementia. Eventually, she began to wander around for hours on end, as if looking for something, during both day and night. It was no use locking her in the house. Once she tried to get outside through a second-floor window; she slipped on a ladder, fell and received a severe cut on her head. This is what Mrs H. had come to. She had been a master teacher of flower arrangement and tea ceremony with over five hundred students, but now she was completely lost.

His wife's illness made Mr H. deeply ponder the meaning of marriage and of life, and that struggle for answers led him to join the Soka Gakkai. He prayed for his wife's recovery, and gradually his own attitude began to change. He watched his wife one night snoring away peacefully and thought how sweet she looked. He was startled to observe the changes that were taking place in his own heart, as he experienced feelings he had never known before. He keenly realised how painful it was for a sick person to be unable to leave the house, so he began taking his wife outside, never missing a day.

MATSUMOTO: You can sense how much he loved her.

KOJIMA: Then, one day, when they were riding a train together, Mrs H. turned to her husband and began to scold him, "How dare you take me to this kind of place? I'm going to tell everyone!" Such outbursts, of course, are characteristic of dementia. Mr H. admitted that, as he endured the curious stares of his fellow passengers, for a moment he felt a shock of anger and shame.

He remained confused and upset. Then, while praying deeply, he realised: Had he ever asked himself what his wife was feeling as she scolded him? He strongly felt, he said, that life was made up of each passing moment. Since that was the case, he must make each moment of his wife's life truly precious. How could he do that? By bringing his wife, moment by moment, whatever joy or pleasure he could.

"At the core of my love for my wife, I sensed the great mercy and compassion of the Gohonzon," he related. "The more I prayed, the more my heart was purified, and the deeper my love for her became." From that time on, until his wife passed away, Mr H. nursed his wife tirelessly, always making a conscious effort to know what she was feeling and thinking.

Six years after the onset of senile dementia, Mrs H. passed away peacefully. In death, her face was so beautiful and serene. Indeed, so radiant and alive was her complexion, that it seemed she might still speak at any moment.

Mr H. said, "In our forty-five years of married life, it was only after my wife became sick that we really came to know each other. I truly believe that was our best time together as husband and wife."

PRESIDENT IKEDA: What a beautiful story! Prayer does deepen our hearts. It is important in any relationship with others to polish the mirror of our heart so we understand other's thoughts and feeling as if they were our own.

As we saw in the story you just related, many patients suffering from senile dementia begin to roam about as their symptoms advance, don't they?

MATSUMOTO: Yes, various symptoms begin to appear, among them wandering, talking to oneself, irrational outbursts, delirium, paranoia, eating strange things, overeating and incontinence.

PRESIDENT IKEDA: What are some practical approaches to dealing with these symptoms?

KOJIMA: Mr H.'s wife began roaming about aimlessly. This is extremely dangerous. The patient can easily get lost or be involved in an accident. On the other hand, if you do not allow the patient to go outside, their condition often worsens.

MATSUMOTO: It is very useful to sew a tag onto their clothing listing their name and address, as well as the telephone number of a family member or relative who can be contacted in case of just such an emergency. If possible, one should never leave the patient alone or unwatched. This will prevent accidents and provide a sense of security.

INAMITSU: It can also be helpful to let the neighbours know about the person's condition and ask them to call you if they see the person out walking alone.

PRESIDENT IKEDA: Some families are ashamed to have a senile family member, and keep them hidden and lock-up in the house. Senile dementia is an illness. It is absolutely not something to be ashamed of. Rather, it is better to explain the patient's condition to your neighbours. Their understanding will put them at ease and it will also win you their cooperation in watching over the person.

Kojima: Yes. The help of neighbours can be indispensable in caring for those with dementia. By far in most cases, bravely bringing the problem out into the open and telling your neighbours will be good for all concerned.

President Ikeda: When Mrs H. began scolding her husband in the train — is that what you mean by irrational outbursts?

Inamitsu: Yes. And, when the patient starts making wild claims like, "The house is falling down!" or "I am going to be killed!" they are evidencing delirium. There is always a reason behind such a behaviour. If we are able to react not to the words and actions themselves but to the feelings behind them, the symptoms are relieved and sometimes even cured.

Matsumoto: One of the characteristics of dementia is that the symptoms appear most strongly in front of the people that the patient trusts. People with this dis-order feel able to say what they want freely to those who take care of them everyday.

Some families are ashamed to have a senile family member, and keep them hidden and lock-up in the house. Senile dementia is an illness. It is absolutely not something to be ashamed of. Rather, it is better to explain the patient's condition to your neighbours. Their understanding will put them at ease and it will also win you their cooperation in watching over the person.

Kojima: In many instances, irrational outbursts and delirium occur because the past and the present are all mixed up in the patient's mind. Something in the present triggers past feelings, such as a loud crash setting off memories of war, making the patient want to flee.

Be Accepting and Respectful

President Ikeda: How can these episodes be handled successfully?

Kojima: Do not panic, and stay by the patient's side, going through the motions together with them. Anxiety is what sets off most attacks, so turn off the television, the vacuum cleaner, or the washing machine, and create a quiet environment. To ease their anxiety, hold their hand, comfortingly rub their back, and offer a sympathetic ear to what is worrying them.

MATSUMOTO: Many people with senile dementia will ask right after finishing a meal, "When are we going to eat?" A nervous disorder makes them unable to feel full, or they forget that they have just eaten. The best approach to this problem is to ask, "What would you like to have?" and encourage the person to think about the kind of food they would like. Then ask how it should be prepared, and ask them to wait a while. This interaction is often enough to satisfy the patient.

PRESIDENT IKEDA: Such nursing is really a tremendously challenging task, but the best thing to do is, as much as possible, to let the patient have his or her own way. Nothing good will come of ignoring or making fun of them, or pointing out the contradictions in what they say. In fact, one can work on improving oneself as a person by always treating the person who is ill with love and respect. Find something that the patient is good at or proud of, even if a long time ago, and talk about that.

When the Patient Asks, "Who Are You?"

PRESIDENT IKEDA: Some people with senile dementia suddenly announce, "I'm going home," even though they are already there.

INAMITSU: Yes. The best approach to this is to humour them. You can ask, "Why don't you stay one more night?" or offer to see them home tomorrow.

KOJIMA: If they still want to leave, offer to take them and go out and take a walk around the neighbourhood for a while before returning home. Then everyone at home should say, "Welcome back! We are waiting for you." This will usually set their mind at ease.

PRESIDENT IKEDA: Many with senile dementia forget their family members' names, don't they?

KOJIMA: When a patient suddenly asks, "Who are you?" many family members are startled. But when you are asked this, you should address the person clearly and state who you are, for example, "Dad, I'm your son, Jack," including both your name and your relationship to them.

INAMITSU: Other good ways of keeping the person in touch with reality are to talk to them and remind them of the time of day. In the morning, say, "Good morning, it is time to get up!" Around midday, say "It is lunch time. Let us eat." And in the evening, "It is night, so let us go to bed." Keep a calendar conspicuously displayed and cross out each day as it passes, so they know what day of the week it is.

MATSUMOTO: There are some drugs that are effective in alleviating certain symptoms of dementia. Though it is not good to rely too much on drugs, temporary use may stabilise a patient's condition and prevent further deterioration.

> Other good ways of keeping the person in touch with reality are to talk to them and remind them of the time of day. In the morning, say, "Good morning, it is time to get up!" Around midday, say "It is lunch time. Let us eat." And in the evening, "It is night, so let us go to bed."

Using Public Health-care Services

PRESIDENT IKEDA: Can families avail themselves of public health-care services to assist with the nursing of patients with senile dementia, as they can for the elderly?

INAMITSU: It depends upon the patient's condition, but basically they can. It is best to start by talking with your doctor or health-care worker.

In particular, if, while the patient's symptoms are still mild, the family avails themselves of day-care services, which teach patients to take care of their daily needs, or of short-stay services, where patients can be cared for on a temporary basis by professional health-care staff, it can help prevent the worsening of symptoms. This also gives the family the opportunity to confer with and seek advice from professionals specialising in this kind of nursing care.

KOJIMA: Senile dementia is going to be an increasing problem as Japan's society ages, but we have yet to address the issue properly as a society.

The Prevention of Senile Dementia

PRESIDENT IKEDA: How can dementia be prevented?

INAMITSU: In the case of multi-infarct dementia, it means preventing strokes and other vascular diseases, such as cerebral arteriosclerosis. The best way is to avoid a diet with too much salt and fat, and monitoring carefully for high blood pressure and diabetes.

PRESIDENT IKEDA: Staying physically active — especially maintaining the physical dexterity of our hands and the mobility of our legs — as well as meeting and socialising with others also keep the brain young.

MATSUMOTO: Yes. Creative hobbies, such as painting or crafts, as well as writing, such as keeping a diary or writing letters, also keep the mind active. Using our voice — speaking, conversing with others and singing are also helpful.

INAMITSU: Moderate exercise is also indispensable in preventing senility. Walking is fine, but tasks that actually contribute to the family welfare, such as shopping, cleaning, and doing the washing, give the patient a sense of purpose and accomplishment.

KOJIMA: Moving residences or renovating the home of an elderly person can trigger the onset of dementia. Some might think it would offer a welcome change of pace and stimulus, but such major changes often confuse the elderly.

PRESIDENT IKEDA: Yes, it is true that sudden changes in an elderly person's environment can lead to various abnormalities manifesting in their physical and mental condition. It is like changing the water in a fish pond. The fish in the pond have got used to their water, and changing it can make them sick.

The human heart is a delicate thing, and the most unexpected thing can cause a person to feel lonely and isolated. There are people who are glad to be living with their grandchildren, but then get depressed when the same grandchildren make fun of their infirmities. When given a nice new room with the best of intentions, some people are not pleased and think instead that they are being deliberately separated from the rest of the household.

MATSUMOTO: The most important thing is to maintain warm communication. It provides the person with senile dementia with a sense of security.

Life after Retirement

PRESIDENT IKEDA: Some traumatic experience or worry can eat away at a person and act as a trigger for senile dementia, can't it? In many cases, retirement often triggers senility, I have heard.

INAMITSU: Those who have made their jobs their lives are particularly affected in this way because they lose their social role, and sense of purpose and satisfaction when they retire.

MATSUMOTO: Yes, senility is often caused by the loss of some useful role. In Japan, for instance, many elderly women who once used to manage their own households begin to manifest signs of senility when they move in to live with a married son or daughter and no longer have such day-to-day responsibilities to perform.

> The human heart is a delicate thing, and the most unexpected thing can cause a person to feel lonely and isolated. There are people who are glad to be living with their grandchildren, but then get depressed when the same grandchildren make fun of their infirmities. When given a nice new room with the best of intentions, some people are not pleased and think instead that they are being deliberately separated from the rest of the household.

PRESIDENT IKEDA: If our school years are our first stage of life and the years after that our second stage of life, then our retirement years, when we put the finishing touch on our lives, are our third stage of life. Though our bodies may be weaker, as long as we set our minds to it we can still make our lives shine.

A positive attitude — "The future awaits me, I have new goals, and I'm going to meet them!" — stimulates the brain cells and gives us new energy. Tsunesaburo Makiguchi, the 1st president of Soka Gakkai, was still studying English after the age of fifty and, in his sixties and seventies, his activities rivalled those of a youth in their passion and energy.

Matsumoto: What wonderful spiritual strength!

Kojima: It is true that those who have a clear purpose in life tend to remain energetic even as they grow older.

President Ikeda: As age exacts its toll, our memories may begin to fail us but our overall judgment, ability to understand others, our knowledge about life, are superior to young people. We reach the age when we can make the most of those abilities earned and honed by experience.

Old age is the time, more than any other period in our lives, when we must ask ourselves about our worth as a human being. Do we still have something of value in our hearts, apart from social prestige and position? In that sense, prevention of mental deterioration and senility start while we are still young. I think we can say it has a deep relationship to how we live our lives as a whole.

Of couse, senile dementia is a disease, and what I am saying does not apply to that.

It is said, however, that those who are less likely to become senile are people who, (1) read newspapers and books, and continue to use their minds; (2) do not complain and fret about every little thing; (3) are not selfish and enjoy caring for others; (4) are warmly sensitive, able to rejoice and delight over things; and (5) have goals and a strong desire to improve themselves.

Matsumoto: Yes. I think that is why SGI activities can help prevent senility.

President Ikeda: As members of the Soka Gakkai, everyday we read the *Seikyo Shimbun* and other publications. We strive to surmount problems through the practice of faith. We talk to people about our experiences and exert ourselves tirelessly for the happiness of others. We are moved and inspired when we see how friends have revitalised their lives through faith. We taste life's joy and exhilaration. Our hearts, minds and bodies do not have time to rust. At the basis of everything, of course, lies *daimoku*. There is no medicine more wondrous or effective than *daimoku* for revitalising our lives. Nothing is ever wasted in our activities for *kosen-rufu*[4] — such

---

4. *Kosen-rufu*: Literally, to 'widely declare and spread (Buddhism)'. To secure lasting peace and happiness for all humankind through the propagation of Nichiren Daishonin's Buddhism.

activities surely constitute the most excellent regimen for good health we can find.

INAMITSU: It is also said that people who have others to talk to are less likely to become senile, too.

KOJIMA: That is another wonderful thing about the SGI organisation.

PRESIDENT IKEDA: Exactly. I hope all our members will establish a daily rhythm conducive to good health within our shared rhythm of *kosen-rufu*, and live cheerful and vital lives, true to themselves. I hope they will all live long and happily.

Buddhism teaches that we will grow younger and our good fortune will accumulate (cf *WND*, pg 464). A new sun rises everyday in the lives of those who practise the Mystic Law. A rich, vibrant life force surges forth within them. They burn with hope, eager to fulfil their mission throughout the three existences of past, present and future. Thus, their hearts grow younger with each passing year and their good fortune increases.

By living each day to the fullest, to the very end, may we bring our lives to a magnificent close like majestic golden rays illuminating the sky in all directions at sunset.

Kidney Disease

Participants in this discussion on
' Humanism and the Art of Medicine:
A New Century of Health'
are SGI President Ikeda, Soka Gakkai
Doctors' Division Leaders Dr Shuhei Morita,
Vice-Secretary Dr Akihiro Tojo
and Kanagawa General Prefecture
Doctors' Division Vice-Secretary
Dr Shosaku Narumi

President Ikeda: In Japanese, a common expression for 'crucial importance' (*kanjin*) is written with the Chinese characters for 'liver' and 'kidneys'. This is said to derive from the fact that our liver and kidneys together form a vital source of our body's energy and vitality. They are, of course, included among the 'five internal organs' of prime importance in traditional Chinese medicine.

Morita: That is true. Traditional Chinese medicine stresses five main internal organs: the heart, the liver, the lungs, the spleen and the kidneys. The liver and kidneys are regarded as especially important organs.

President Ikeda: That is how something of 'crucial importance' came to be referred to in Japanese by a term that combines the Chinese characters for those two vital organs.

And, it is probably because our kidneys have an especially indispensable function that we have two of them — that way, if for some reason one kidney fails, we have a spare.

Today, we have kidney specialists, Dr Akihiro Tojo and Dr Shosaku Narumi, with us. I look forward to your contributions to our discussion.

Tojo and Narumi: We are very glad to be here.

President Ikeda: Let us begin then. Is there any easy way to know if the kidneys are malfunctioning?

Tojo: Yes. We can judge the health of our kidneys, at least to a certain extent, by our urine.

President Ikeda: Even in ancient Greece, I understand, the state of a person's urine was regarded as a sort of barometer of health, wasn't it? One way it was tested in those days, I believe, was to stir it with a piece of straw and see how viscous it was. If I am correct, the founder of Western medicine, Hippocrates, also wrote about irregularities in the urine.

Tojo: Yes, he did. Among his remarks were statements that pale-coloured urine or urine that formed a froth were signs of some disorder.

President Ikeda: Are those statements true even from the perspective of modern medicine? Granted, of course, that we shouldn't jump to hasty

Traditional Chinese medicine stresses five main internal organs: the heart, the liver, the lungs, the spleen and the kidneys. The liver and kidneys are regarded as especially important organs.

conclusions based on our own self-diagnosis.

NARUMI: Healthy urine is clear and a light yellow colour. Just because it seems pale does not necessary mean that there is anything wrong.

PRESIDENT IKEDA: I see. How about foaming urine?

TOJO: When foam stays on the urine for a long time, it can mean that protein or glucose is mixed with it, and that is a warning sign.

NARUMI: Still, after vigorous exercise or when running a fever, even a healthy person may have protein in their urine.

PRESIDENT IKEDA: What about the presence of blood in the urine?

TOJO: Well, it is rare to find urine so bloody that it is bright red. In some cases, urine containing blood is a brown colour, like tea. But often blood in the urine cannot be detected with the naked eye.

PRESIDENT IKEDA: What sorts of diseases can cause blood to be present in the urine?

Tojo: Many diseases can cause blood to appear in the urine, including acute and chronic nephritis (inflammation of the kidneys), kidney stones, or cancer of the kidneys or bladder.

President Ikeda: What about cloudy urine?

Narumi: Cloudy urine is an indication of a urinary tract infection (ie, an infection in any part of the urine-collecting system which can involve kidneys, bladder, etc).

President Ikeda: Can there be a problem when the amount of urine one is passing is too small?

Narumi: A sudden, dramatic decrease in urine can signal acute renal (kidney) failure. A large amount of urine, on the other hand, can be a sign of diabetes mellitus, diabetes insipidus, or chronic nephritis.

President Ikeda: Some people seem to be bothered by an overly frequent need to urinate.

Narumi: That can be a sign of cystitis (inflammation and infection of the bladder) in women, or of prostate enlargement in men, particulary if the latter are middle-aged or older.

Tojo: Most cases of cystitis are accompanied by the sensation of having to empty one's bladder, even if you have just done so, or a need to urinate frequently, at intervals, say, of less than two hours.

Morita: In many older men, enlargement of the prostate gland, which is located at the exit of the bladder, constricts the passage of urine so that it takes longer to urinate, and often causes them to wake up in the middle of the night with the need to urinate.

President Ikeda: The kidneys are the body's 'urine-producing factory', eliminating its waste products. How do they work?

Tojo: About one-fourth of the blood pumped by the heart passes through the kidneys. That amounts to about 1,500 litres (approximately 400 gallons) a day. The kidneys filter out waste products from the blood and produce about

SGI President Ikeda (right), Soka Gakkai Doctors' Division Leaders Dr Shuhei Morita (2nd right), Vice-Secretary Dr Akihiro Tojo (2nd left) and Kanagawa General Prefecture Doctors' Division Vice-Secretary Dr Shosaku Narumi (left).

150 litres (40 gallons) of filtrate in a 24-hour period.

PRESIDENT IKEDA: That is quite a large amount! When we say 150 litres (40 gallons), that is the amount it takes to fill a steel oil drum, right?

MORITA: If we had to eliminate 150 litres of urine each day, we would have to spend the entire day in the bathroom!

NARUMI: Yes. Of the water filtered from the bloodstream by the kidneys, ie, the filtrate, only about one per cent — around 1.5 litres (2.5 pints) — is discharged as urine. The remaining 99 per cent of water and nutrients that are essential to the body are recycled by the kidneys and returned to the bloodstream.

PRESIDENT IKEDA: Ninety-nine per cent is recycled? What an efficient factory! What is the process through which the kidneys filter the blood to produce urine?

TOJO: First, the kidneys filter the blood through the biological filter of the glomerulus, a cluster of microscopic capillaries. Each kidney has about a million glomeruli, as these blood vessels are known individually.

PRESIDENT IKEDA: Where does the term *glomerulus* come from?

MORITA: It comes from Latin and means "in the form of a ball." The glomeruli wind together to form a ball-shaped cluster, which is how the glomerulus gets its name.

TOJO: The glomerulus produces the filtrate, which is then concentrated more than a hundred times in the renal tubules.

NARUMI: While the filtrate is passing through the renal tubules, the reusable 99 per cent — for example, water, amino acids, sodium and glucose — is reabsorbed for recycling through the walls of the renal tubules.

PRESIDENT IKEDA: The living organism that is our body wastes nothing. It tries to make the best use of everything to the furthest possible extent. It isn't recklessly wasteful. It is always seeking to produce value, in its own marvellous fashion. It is truly awesome. This drive to create value is none other than life force. And, one of the reasons we practise Nichiren Daishonin's Buddhism is to strengthen our life force.

By the way, do the kidneys have any other functions?

NARUMI: In addition to their function of ridding the body of wastes, they help preserve the proper balance of sodium and water in our bodies and regulate our blood pressure. They also secrete erythropoietin, a hormone that is important in the formation of haemoglobin and red blood cells, and the metabolically active form of vitamin D, which helps the body absorb calcium.

PRESIDENT IKEDA: They certainly have many different functions, don't they?

MORITA: Yes, indeed. These small, bean-shaped organs, each of which is only about the size of a person's fist, play a vital role in preserving a constant, balanced internal environment in our bodies — in other words, our electrolyte balance, the concentration of water and sodium, and homeostasis.

PRESIDENT IKEDA: The kidneys are hard workers. You mentioned earlier that they play a role in controlling blood pressure, I believe.

Tojo: The kidneys secrete a hormone that regulates blood pressure. Also, when kidney function deteriorates, it can lead to the failure of the proper excretion of excess water and sodium in the body as urine, and their retention in the blood vessels contributes to high blood pressure.

President Ikeda: People say that when your kidneys are not working well, it shows in your complexion.

Narumi: Yes. That is because when a person's kidneys are not functioning well, they are likely to suffer from anaemia. The bones also become more brittle. These are the results of the kidneys' failure to produce erythropoietin and the metabolically active form of vitamin D, which contribute to production of blood and formation of bone, respectively.

President Ikeda: The kidneys are really important in a wide variety of bodily functions. From ancient times, they have been regarded as the 'storehouse of vital energy', and we can see that there is considerable truth to that belief.
   Since they are so important, any damage to the kidneys must affect all the other organs and severely disable the entire human body.

Tojo: Precisely.

President Ikeda: What kinds of kidney diseases are there?

Morita: Well, for starters there are acute and chronic nephritis.

Tojo: Most cases of acute nephritis are triggered by colds. Just about when cold symptoms, such as sore throat and fever have receded, the eyelids and extremities swell. The amount of urine may suddenly decrease, or blood may appear in it. Blood pressure also rises.

Narumi: Even a healthy person will experience swelling in the feet or ankles if they stand for a long period of time. But if swelling is evident when one first gets up in the morning, it may be a sign of illness.

Morita: Swelling is a symptom of several illnesses in addition to kidney disease, including heart disease and cirrhosis of the liver.

President Ikeda: What is the cause of acute nephritis?

NARUMI: The most common cause is bacterial infection of the glomerulus, which impairs its function.

MORITA: Most kidney diseases are the result of some problem affecting the glomerulus. When this happens, the glomerulus fails to filter out fairly large particles, such as proteins, as it normally would, and allows them to pass into the urine.

TOJO: Fortunately, with appropriate treatment acute nephritis can be cured.

PRESIDENT IKEDA: How about chronic nephritis?

TOJO: It, too, is caused by various malfunctions in the glomerulus, according to which it is categorised into different types of disorder. And unfortunately, sometimes, the causes are not clear.

PRESIDENT IKEDA: The symptoms are the same as acute nephritis? Protein and blood in the urine, swelling, and so forth?

NARUMI: Yes. But the condition progresses slowly, so the person is almost unaware of it. Most patients only learn they have the disease during a regular check-up. The kidneys and liver are often called 'the silent organs'. By the time we ourselves notice that something is wrong with them, the disease is usually quite far advanced. That is why regular medical check-ups are so important.

PRESIDENT IKEDA: In the past, it was believed that chronic nephritis could never be cured.

TOJO: There are two types of chronic nephritis — one which does not progress very much and one which does. The former often heals on its own. But if the second type is left untreated, it may result in renal failure, in which the kidneys nearly cease to function.

PRESIDENT IKEDA: Renal failure necessitates dialysis, doesn't it?

TOJO: Yes, or a kidney transplant. But in Japan, dialysis is by far the most common treatment. It places a great burden on the patient, who must undergo four to five-hour sessions of dialysis two or three times a week.

Tojo: The knowledge that one must continue this treatment for the rest of one's life takes a heavy toll mentally and emotionally as well.

President Ikeda: Nothing is more painful than illness, and nothing is more precious than health. I hope that all who are enduring such suffering will say to themselves, "I will definitely get better!" and focus constructively on what they can do now, in their present state. For example, if they cannot work as others do, they can concentrate on deepening their inner selves, so that they live profound and inspiring lives. They can make themselves into examples for others, so that others will say, "I want to live my life with the kind of spirit that they do." When that is your goal, you are living a truly healthy life, whether you are suffering from illness or not.

It is also important that co-workers, friends and neighbours encourage and support someone battling illness.

> **Nothing is more painful than illness, and nothing is more precious than health. I hope that all who are enduring such suffering will say to themselves, "I will definitely get better!" and focus constructively on what they can do now, in their present state.**

Morita: Those suffering from kidney disease need to live at a relaxed pace, free of stress and tension.

President Ikeda: What other kidney diseases are there?

Tojo: Nephrotic syndrome is another common one. The cause is not yet known, but malfunctions in the glomerulus cause the passing of large amounts of protein in the urine and severe swelling (edema).

Narumi: Recently, in Japan, we have seen a significant and disturbing increase in diabetic nephropathy — abnormal changes caused to the kidneys as a result of long-standing diabetes mellitus. The capillaries of the glomerulus malfunction and the kidneys no longer filter properly. As a result, much protein is passed in the urine and, renal failure can occur.

President Ikeda: There are also kidney stones to worry about.

Tojo: Yes. Kidney stones are formed when the contents of the urine concrete into small particles as hard as stones. Similar stones can also form in other parts of the urinary tract, including the ureter, bladder and urethra, for example.

PRESIDENT IKEDA: They say nothing is more excruciating than the pain caused by such a stone.

MORITA: Stones obstructing the ureter, the thin tubular portion connecting the kidneys and bladder, can be especially painful, causing severe pain from the back to the waist. So, in short, yes, stones can be excruciating, and they can also cause blood to appear in the urine.

NARUMI: Drinking plenty of water and getting the right amount of exercise are good ways to prevent the formation of stones.

PRESIDENT IKEDA: What should we know about preventing and treating kidney diseases?

TOJO: In our daily lives, three things can badly affect our kidneys: (1) colds, (2) exhaustion and stress, and (3) chills.

NARUMI: As we mentioned earlier, a cold often triggers acute nephritis or its reoccurrence. Exhaustion, stress and chills hamper the circulation of blood in the kidneys.

TOJO: Sufficient rest and staying warm are very important, as are maintaining a healthy routine which will increase our resistance to infections. Going to bed at a reasonable hour and getting enough sleep are also crucial.

PRESIDENT IKEDA: How about exercise?

TOJO: Kidney diseases can raise the blood pressure, so strenuous exercise should be avoided, particularly in the case of the elderly.

MORITA: Monitoring blood pressure is indispensable in preventing and treating kidney disease. High blood pressure places an extra burden on the kidneys, so it is important to control it.

NARUMI: There is a strong connection between kidney disease and conditions, such as high blood pressure and diabetes. Weight control is also an important factor for preventing kidney problems.

PRESIDENT IKEDA: What should people with weak kidneys pay special attention to as far as diet is concerned?

TOJO: First, they should reduce their salt intake. Too much salt can lead to water retention and also raises blood pressure.

NARUMI: Reducing protein intake is also a good idea — remembering, of course, that the body needs protein and one should not reduce it too much.

MORITA: Treatment of kidney diseases is usually long term, and it differs depending upon the type of illness and the severity of the symptoms. The best thing is to consult your physician.

TOJO: I know I am repeating myself, but one cannot overemphasise the importance of regular medical examinations, including urine tests.

PRESIDENT IKEDA: At the beginning of our discussion, we mentioned the 'five internal organs'. Buddhism links these five internal organs to the five elements. The ancients of the East categorised all things in terms of the five elements of earth, water, fire, wind and void. And, Nichiren Daishonin said that the five elements were the five characters of the title of the Lotus Sutra.

In the Gosho, the Daishonin writes, "At present, the entire body of Honourable Abutsu is composed of the five elements of earth, water, fire, wind and space [ku]. These five elements are also the five characters of the daimoku [Nam-myoho-renge-kyo]." (WND, pg 299)

A life based on the Mystic Law, a practice where 'faith equals daily life', makes all parts of the microcosm that is our individual life, including our five organs, function soundly and vibrantly. The path of the Mystic Law is the fundamental path to health and to happiness.

Skin Disorders

Participants in this discussion on
' Humanism and the Art of Medicine:
A New Century of Health'
are SGI President Ikeda and dermatologists,
Dr Chiaki Nishiyama and Dr Kimiko Sato,
both of them are the Soka Gakkai
Doctors' Division Leaders

PRESIDENT IKEDA: Dr Sato, Dr Nishiyama, both of you are dermatologists. Why did you choose the field of dermatology?

SATO: I came down with nephritis while I was a medical student. I was so sick that for a time I was told that I would not be able to withstand the pressures and demands of being a doctor. I tried to think of a field of specialization that did not require great physical stamina, and that was how I chose dermatology.

NISHIYAMA: When I was a medical student, I broke out in a rash from a chemical called formalin that was used during anatomy class. My father was a doctor, too, but unfortunately not a dermatologist! I must have been in pain for about a year and a half. But then I went to a dermatologist, and I was cured in just two weeks. That is when I decided that I wanted to become a dermatologist.

PRESIDENT IKEDA: Once when I was a child, I had a large boil under my chin. It swelled up tremendously, and was beginning to affect the bone. I tried various medicines, but nothing worked. There were no dermatologists nearby. Finally, I had to go to a regional hospital and have it incised, but it took a very long time to heal. It hurt, it was swollen, and I didn't want to go to school, where everyone would notice it.

In the old days, children often suffered from boils, but we do not see that so frequently any more.

NISHIYAMA: Nutrition has improved for one thing, and we have many new drugs. Today, there has been a dramatic decrease in such skin disorders.

PRESIDENT IKEDA: I have heard it said that the body's largest organ is not the lungs or the liver but, in fact, the skin!

SATO: Yes, that is true. An average adult has approximately 1.6 square metres (17 square feet) of skin. And, while the average adult heart weighs about 300 grams (10½ oz) and the liver about 1.5 kilograms (3 lb 3 oz), the skin weighs as much as 4 kilograms (8 lb 12 oz).

PRESIDENT IKEDA: We talk about someone being 'thick-skinned', meaning insensitive, but is there actually a difference in skin thickness from individual to individual?

SGI President Ikeda (Left) with dermatologists, Dr Chiaki Nishiyama (centre) and Dr Kimiko Sato (right), both of them are the Soka Gakkai Doctors' Division vice-leaders.

NISHIYAMA: Medically speaking, there is no relationship between the thickness of a person's skin and his or her character! A 'thick-skinned' person and a 'thin-skinned' person alike have skin about 1 millimetre (0.04 inch) thick on the face, while on the rest of the body, it averages about 2 millimetres (0.08 inch).

PRESIDENT IKEDA: What are the functions of the skin?

SATO: Protection, secretion and excretion, heat regulation, and sensation.

PRESIDENT IKEDA: My, that is a pretty hardworking 2 millimetres!

SATO: It is indeed. The first function of the skin is to protect the body. It acts like a cushion that absorbs force when we bump into, scrape against, or are impacted by an object. Though the skin may be damaged in the process, it has the ability to repair itself.

NISHIYAMA: The skin also blocks out bacteria, chemicals, such as soap, and ultraviolet rays. It serves as a protective barrier.

PRESIDENT IKEDA: When you say secretion and excretion, are you referring to perspiration?

SATO: Yes. Perspiration contains not only water and salt but waste products that the body no longer needs. On average, we perspire about 1.5 litres (3 pints) a day — about the same as the average amount of urine we pass each day.

NISHIYAMA: The skin also eliminates any toxic materials from the body, in addition to perspiration. In 1968, there was a food-poisoning incident in which rice-bran oil was contaminated with a toxic substance[1] (the Kanemi oil-poisoning incident). All the victims, regardless of age, broke out in pimple-like pustules. An examination of the pustules by dermatologists at a local university hospital revealed that the body was excreting the toxin from the pores, which caused the pustules to form.

PRESIDENT IKEDA: Yes, that was a famous incident. It worried us all a great deal at the time.

Perspiration is also a way of lowering the body temperature, isn't it?

SATO: Yes, it is. A perspiring person may appear to be hot, but actually the opposite is true. When we perspire, the evaporation of the perspiration from our skin's surface cools us, lowering the body temperature. This is how the skin helps regulate body temperature. When it is cold, the blood vessels in our skin contract to allow only a small amount of blood through them, promoting conservation of body heat. When it is hot, the blood vessels expand to permit blood to flow freely, facilitating evaporation of perspiration.

PRESIDENT IKEDA: All these things take place without our being consciously aware of them — how wondrous are the workings inherent in life!

SATO: Another function of the skin is to sense pain, heat, cold and other phenomena.

PRESIDENT IKEDA: Apparently, the human race has suffered from skin diseases from ancient times. Egyptian papyruses record skin cancer, eczema, carbuncles and other disorders.

About how many different kinds of skin diseases are there?

---

1. Polychlorinated biphenals (PCBs).

Perspiration contains not only water and salt but waste products that the body no longer needs. On average, we perspire about 1.5 litres (3 pints) a day — about the same as the average amount of urine we pass each day.

SATO: More than nine hundred types are recognised.

PRESIDENT IKEDA: What kind of skin diseases are on the increase lately?

SATO: Atopic eczema and other diseases that are related to the immune system and allergies.

PRESIDENT IKEDA: We have already discussed atopic eczema in this series. That particular instalment drew a great response from our readers.

What other skin diseases are prevalent?

NISHIYAMA: Most frequently encountered are eczema-type disorders, such as contact dermatitis, especially hand dermatitis, and various kinds of rashes. They account for nearly a third of all skin diseases.

SATO: Rashes are generally caused by contact with some irritant. Common irritants are metal jewellery, such as necklaces or watch bands, or plants, such as poison sumac, ginkgo and primrose, as well as certain industrial chemicals. The skin that comes into contact with the irritant turns red and swells up, becoming extremely itchy at the same time.

In some cases, a single contact causes no reaction, but repeated contact can produce a rash. Perspiration can also worsen the symptoms.

PRESIDENT IKEDA: What precisely causes eczema on the hands?

NISHIYAMA: Eczema on the hands occurs most frequently among people who are always exposing their hands to soaps, detergents and other chemical solvents in their work. The skin of the palm and fingers becomes rough, and sometimes the fingerprints even disappear. In some cases, the back of the hands and the area around the fingernails becomes red and extremely itchy.

PRESIDENT IKEDA: How is eczema different from hives?

SATO: In both cases, the skin is itchy and red, but in the case of hives the symptoms disappear in just a few hours.
   Middle-aged and elderly people often suffer from pruritus (itchiness), which is characterised by an itchiness all over the body, but is not accompanied by any rash.

NISHIYAMA: Some skin diseases are caused by viruses. Shingles (herpes zoster) is a good example. It usually occurs in people who have had chicken pox as a child. The virus remains dormant in their bodies, and when they reach middle age or older and their resistance naturally lowers, the virus becomes active again, causing a rash to break out. A characteristic feature of shingles is that it is accompanied by intense neuralgic pain.

SATO: Most warts on the hands and feet are also caused by viruses. Warts in elderly people, however, are often part of the natural ageing process.

PRESIDENT IKEDA: Scabies is another common skin disease, isn't it?

SATO: Scabies is caused by a parasitic insect, the scabies mite (*Sarcoptes scabiei*).

PRESIDENT IKEDA: Napoleon suffered badly from scabies, which he caught from his soldiers. There is a well-known episode about him and this disorder. Scabies, also called 'the itch', was rampant in Europe at the time, but its cause was unknown. Many doctors, when confronted with a disease that they could find no cause for, simply blamed it on scabies. One day, Napoleon caught a cold while on the battlefield. His symptoms were not quite typical, so the military doctor, puzzled, adopted the common excuse and told

Napoleon that his internal organs had been attacked by scabies.

What the doctor did not realise was that Napoleon actually did suffer from scabies. Napoleon evidently saw through the doctor's temporising. He smiled cynically and said, "You are indeed a great doctor, since without knowing that I actually suffer from scabies, you were able to diagnose my trouble with such great dispatch!"

NISHIYAMA: The great doctor was a great 'doctorer', it seems!

PRESIDENT IKEDA: In any situation, knowledge and correct information are very important. Without them, we can be easily led astray. How much more important this is in matters of health, which can mean the difference between life and death.

We have said this on many occasions during this series, but it truly is important to take charge of one's own health, not to leave it up to others. We must become doctor, nurse and patient all rolled into one, and work wisely to protect our health. To do that, we need to be properly informed about health issues, and to make certain we always receive a thorough explanation from our doctors.

What can we do to keep our skin healthy?

SATO: The basics are the same in preventing every disease: to have a balanced diet and keep a balanced and healthy lifestyle.

PRESIDENT IKEDA: What practical steps can we take to care for our skin?

SATO: Regular cleansing is most important. It is a good idea to get into the habit of washing your hands and face when you come home at the end of the day.

NISHIYAMA: And not just with water, but with soap. Some people say that soap is too dry and harsh on the skin, but if you thoroughly rinse it away, it rarely causes problems.

PRESIDENT IKEDA: I have heard, however, that elderly people should go easy on using soap.

NISHIYAMA: Yes, that is right. Actually, our skin begins to age from around our early thirties, so this advice does not necessarily apply just to senior citizens.

SATO: In healthy skin, the outer layers of the epidermis, rich in lipids, help protect against the evaporation of fluid from within and keep the skin moist and supple. As the skin ages, however, oil secretion decreases and the skin dries out very easily. The overuse of soaps and vigorous rubbing only further deplete the skin's natural oils and exacerbate the dryness.

PRESIDENT IKEDA: I know many elderly people enjoy taking baths daily. Perhaps they would be wise to take note of this point.

NISHIYAMA: Yes, hot water in particular strips the skin of its natural oils. It is better if the elderly bathe in tepid, not hot, water, and stay in the bath only for a short time.

PRESIDENT IKEDA: By the way, do you have any advice for those who suffer from eczema on the hands, an affliction we spoke about a little earlier.

NISHIYAMA: Yes. It is a good idea to wear rubber gloves when using detergents or chemical solvents. It is even more effective when you wear thin cotton gloves underneath the rubber gloves, since many people are prone to rashes from latex as well.

PRESIDENT IKEDA: Ultraviolet sunlight is also harmful to our skin, isn't it?

SATO: Yes. It accelerates the skin's ageing process. Overexposure to the damaging rays of the sun can cause not only wrinkles and freckles, but make our skin more susceptible to warts and skin cancer.

PRESIDENT IKEDA: How can we protect ourselves against ultraviolet rays?

SATO: Basically, by avoiding long exposure to direct sunlight. It is a good idea to wear a hat or use a parasol during the hours when the sun is at its strongest. And, I would also recommend applying sunscreen or wearing a long-sleeved shirt or jacket when spending any length of time outdoors, to

When swimming in an outdoor pool, or at the beach, about thirty minutes in the sun is the maximum of safe exposure.

protect oneself against UV radiation.

President Ikeda: Sunbathing once had a reputation as being very healthful.

Nishiyama: Moderate exposure to the sun can indeed be beneficial, having a germicidal effect. But overexposure only damages the skin. When swimming in an outdoor pool, or at the beach, about thirty minutes in the sun is the maximum of safe exposure.

President Ikeda: In Japan, we often say that people from regions noted for pure water have beautiful skin.

Sato: Yes, hence the reputation of the great beauties of Akita and Kyoto. These regions are also famous for their excellent sáke (Japanese rice wine), the core ingredient of which is said to be pure, good-quality water. The best water for sáke is that which promotes healthy metabolic function; and that is thought to be the reason that such water promotes good skin as well.

President Ikeda: I see. Does stress have any effect on our skin?

Sato: Yes. It does not have the same effect on everyone, but it is true to say that of two people with the same basic skin type, the person subjected to significant stress is more likely to have skin problems. I think we can say, as a result, that a balanced, anxiety-free lifestyle is beneficial to the good health of our skin.

PRESIDENT IKEDA: When one has a skin problem, should one go to see a dermatologist, or should one go to see an internist first?

NISHIYAMA: In very general terms, we can divide skin disorders into two types: those caused by external irritants and those caused by internal problems. I think the best procedure is to have a dermatologist look at the problem first; he or she will then refer you to another department if that is what is called for.

PRESIDENT IKEDA: Our skin is not only an exterior covering but also a mirror that reflects our inner health.

Can a person's overall health be evaluated by looking at their skin?

SATO: Well, some people wear so much make-up nowadays that they can masterfully camouflage a less than healthy complexion! But seriously, the condition of our skin is a barometer of our general health. It is a very good idea to look closely at our skin on a daily basis.

PRESIDENT IKEDA: I think that many of us tend not to pay too much attention to skin problems, thinking they will just go away of their own accord. But really, without being neurotic about it of course, we should keep a close watch on our skin, shouldn't we?

Sariputra, as you may know, was a famous disciple of Sakyamuni, hailed as 'foremost in wisdom'. In a general sense, Sariputra represents all who correctly practise Buddhism.[2] The three Chinese characters that comprise Sariputra's name in Japanese, *Sharihotsu,* have been interpreted respectively to mean skin (*sha*), flesh (*ri*) and bone (*hotsu*), thus representing life in its entirety. The transformation of our lives that we achieve through Buddhist practice affects both our bodies and our minds. Our bodies and our minds are transformed right to their very essence. The life force of the Mystic Law

2. In the *Ongi Kuden (Record of the Orally Transmitted Teachings),* Nichiren Daishonin says, "Now Nichiren and his followers who chant Nam-myoho-renge-kyo are all Sariputras." (*Gosho Zenshu,* pg 722)

pervades and vitalises our flesh, our bones and our skin.

I hope all our readers will spend each day cheerfully and vibrantly, brimming with the dynamic energy of the rising sun, faces radiant with good health. Pursuing the wise path of 'faith equals daily life' is surely the greatest proof of being 'foremost in wisdom'.

Medicines and Drugs

Participants in this discussion on
' Humanism and the Art of Medicine:
A New Century of Health'
are SGI President Ikeda, Soka Gakkai
Doctors' Division Leader Dr Yoshio Kanaya
and pharmacists, Hitomi Kodama
and Yuriko Kato.

PRESIDENT IKEDA: There is such a surge of interest in drugs and medicines that the current 'health boom' in Japan might well be described as a 'medicine boom'. In fact, there are many new drugs on the market, but many of us lack proper information about them. I think that is a fair description of the present situation. With that in mind, we have invited three experts in this area to contribute to today's session.

KANAYA, KODAMA AND KATO: Hello.

PRESIDENT IKEDA: I remember once when I visited the Chinese city of Guilin [in 1980, on the SGI leader's fifth visit to China]. While we were all waiting for our boat, two girls selling medicine approached us. I asked them, jokingly, "Do you have any medicine to make me smarter?" And they answered without a pause, "We just sold out!" I was delighted with their fine sense of humour, their quick wit — just what one would expect from a country like China, with its culture and history.

KANAYA: If you asked that question in Japan, the peddler would probably just answer coldly, "There's no such thing!"

PRESIDENT IKEDA: What exactly is medicine?

KANAYA: In China, they say that anything can be a 'medicine'.

KATO: In Japan, according to the Drugs, Cosmetics and Medical Instruments Act, a 'medicine' is anything that is used to treat, diagnose or prevent illness in humans or animals.

KODAMA: Among all the available drugs and medicines, those that receive the approval of the Ministry of Health and Welfare are classified as pharmaceuticals.

KANAYA: The basic function of drugs and medicines is to assist the body's own powers of healing. A medicine is any substance that acts as an agent in stimulating the body's natural healing powers.

PRESIDENT IKEDA: Yes, that seems like a good definition. Soka Gakkai 2nd president Josei Toda used to say that the human body is one big pharmaceutical factory. Medical science and drugs, he said, should only be

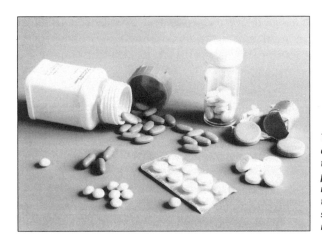

The basic function of drugs and medicines is to assist the body's own powers of healing. A medicine is any substance that acts as an agent in stimulating the body's natural healing powers.

used to assist and enhance the body's own ability to heal itself.

KODAMA: I think that is a very important point. Instead of becoming too dependent upon medication, it is important to try to achieve and preserve a physical condition in which one can get well without resorting to drugs where possible.

PRESIDENT IKEDA: Incidentally, what are the differences between prescription drugs and over-the-counter remedies in Japan?

KODAMA: Prescription drugs, of course, require a doctor's prescription, while over-the-counter drugs don't.

PRESIDENT IKEDA: When we visit our doctor with a cold, he or she often prescribes several different drugs, but when we go to a pharmacy, the pharmacist will usually recommend only one kind of cold medicine. Why is that?

KATO: Most prescription drugs are designed for a single purpose. If you have a fever, a cough and a runny nose, the doctor will prescribe one drug for each symptom.

KODAMA: On the other hand, over-the-counter cold medicines are designed to treat a wide variety of symptoms, so they often contain several drugs combined into one remedy.

KANAYA: To compare drugs to food, we might say that over-the-counter drugs are a sort of 'pre-packaged meal', the same for all, while prescription drugs are a 'home-cooked meal' of fresh ingredients, such as vegetables, meat and fruit, prepared just for the patient.

PRESIDENT IKEDA: I see. The doctor writes a prescription that meets the specific needs of the patient.

KATO: Yes. Though, of course, the actual preparation of the prescription is done by the pharmacist.

KODAMA: The best thing about prescription drugs is that they are prescribed expressly to meet the specific needs of each patient. For example, one patient may have a cold, but no fever, while another has a fever. With prescription drugs, the doctor can prescribe according to the particular symptoms.

KANAYA: The doctor can also respond to the patients' request, such as for a drug that would not cause drowsiness. Such a choice sometimes is not possible with over-the-counter drugs. When you buy a commercial cold medication, you are getting a drug that is also designed to relieve fever even if you do not have one, and all sorts of things you may not need.

PRESIDENT IKEDA: What would you suggest is the best way to use these two sources of medication?

KODAMA: Over-the-counter remedies are useful in an emergency, for example, when you are travelling, or when your symptoms suddenly worsen, and you cannot get to a doctor.

KANAYA: Even then, it is wise not to choose a medicine on your own. Tell the pharmacist your symptoms, and they will recommend the best medicine. And, let them know about any medications you may already be taking for a chronic illness.

KATO: When your symptoms are different than usual or they persist longer than is usual, you should definitely visit your doctor and get a prescription of medicine. In that case, you should also tell your doctor what over-the-counter remedies you may have been taking.

PRESIDENT IKEDA: Some people take over-the-counter medications and prescription medicines at the same time, don't they?

KANAYA: Yes, they do. And, others take several different over-the-counter medicines at the same time. It is very important not to decide on your own what medicines you should take. Always seek the advice of a pharmacist or doctor.

PRESIDENT IKEDA: Nichiren Daishonin said, "To illustrate, when giving medicine to a sick person, one should know what kind of medicine was administered before. Otherwise, different kinds of medicine may conflict and work against one another, killing the patient." (WND, pg 280) The Daishonin was using medicines as a metaphor for the necessity of knowing what philosophies or religions are already current before spreading the True Law.

> Nichiren Daishonin said, "To illustrate, when giving medicine to a sick person, one should know what kind of medicine was administered before. Otherwise, different kinds of medicine may conflict and work against one another, killing the patient." (WND, pg 280) The Daishonin was using medicines as a metaphor for the necessity of knowing what philosophies or religions are already current before spreading the True Law.

KANAYA: Nichiren Daishonin was even aware of the medical science of his time.

PRESIDENT IKEDA: From the time of Sakyamuni, Buddhism has evidenced a strong interest in healing the sufferings of both mind and body, and many Buddhists studied and wrote on medicine. I won't go into the details, but I think we can say that the art of pharmacy is the product of humanity's long struggle with illness. The history of medicinal remedies is as old as the history of our species. The oldest records of medicines are found on clay tablets from Mesopotamia, dating as far back as 2700 BC.

KODAMA: In Sakyamuni's India, many substances were used as medicines, including such plant materials as poppies, oleander, tumeric and sandalwood; animal substances, such as the musk of musk deer; and minerals, such as mercury. With the exception of mercury (which is highly toxic), all those substances are still in use today as medicines.

KATO: Drugs that are derived from living plants and animals are called natural drugs. Many modern pharmaceuticals have been produced from analysing just why it is that such natural drugs are effective.

PRESIDENT IKEDA: The wisdom of the ancients is impressive indeed. Though thousands of years have passed, it still benefits us today.

KANAYA: Yes. But there have also been some very strange medicines. For example, in ancient Mesopotamia, horse manure was regarded as a remedy. I have no idea if it was effective or not, but it was used for a very long time.

PRESIDENT IKEDA: Japanese drugstores carry a wide variety of vitamin and health drinks. Are these classified as medicines?

KANAYA: Some are, and in that case they must be properly labelled. But the rest are really just categorised as soft drinks or 'health foods'.

PRESIDENT IKEDA: Are they still effective, in spite of the fact that they are not medicines?

KATO: They are of no direct help in treating any illness, but they can be used as nutritional supplements after an illness or when one has no appetite.

KODAMA: When we are healthy and have an appetite, we get all the vitamins we need from our food, and such drinks are of little use. Any excess of vitamins ingested is just excreted through urine and faeces.

KANAYA: Vitamins are very important, of course, but many of them, such as vitamins B and C, cannot be stored very long by the body. Daily servings of fruits and vegetables are the best and most balanced way to get enough vitamins.

KATO: Nutritional supplements can be effective when one hasn't had enough sleep or is suffering from fatigue. Of course, the best thing to do when you are tired is to rest.

PRESIDENT IKEDA: But people today are so busy, and often cannot rest even when they want to. Those are the times that they are likely to turn to health drinks, because they are so handy. But if one drinks such supplements to keep going and then gets sick from exhaustion or overwork, then they will have had just the opposite effect that was intended. For the elderly, in particular, rest is important. I hope they will make special efforts to get the rest they need.

The vitamin drinks sold in Japan are based mostly on Western medicine, while the nutritional supplements are based on Chinese medicine. What is the difference between these two medical traditions?

KANAYA: Western medicine focuses on disease, and is designed to treat specific symptoms in specific organs, such as illnesses of the stomach, the eye or the ear. Chinese medicine, on the other hand, focuses on the individual holistically and treats the entire body, rather than specific organs or symptoms, aiming to cure illness by balancing the body's inner harmony and working for a general improvement of the patient's condition.

PRESIDENT IKEDA: It is the difference between looking at the part and looking at the whole, then.

KODAMA: Yes. For example, in Western medicine, there is a specific drug for a specific symptom. Whoever the patient is, pain is treated with analgesics and rash is treated with antihistamines. But that is not the case in Chinese medicine. The same medicine may be prescribed for both joint pain and hives. At the same time, different medicines might be prescribed for different patients, even though they have the same symptoms.

KATO: That is why it is so difficult to answer when someone asks what a particular Chinese medicine is for.

PRESIDENT IKEDA: Are there any other differences?

KANAYA: The drugs themselves are different. Most drugs used in Western medicine consist of a single substance, but the drugs used in Chinese medicine are a combination of many different natural drugs. Of course, each natural drug contains many different substances, so a single Chinese medicine can contain hundreds of substances.

PRESIDENT IKEDA: When I was a child, we were given a medicine called Bear's Gall-bladder (Jpn *kumo no i*) when we had an upset stomach, and it was quite effective. Is that a Chinese medicine?

KODAMA: Bear's Gall-bladder is an ingredient used in the preparations of many Chinese medicines.

PRESIDENT IKEDA: Do the drugs of both Western and Chinese medicine have side effects?

KATO: Yes, they do. Western drugs affect not only the organ they are aimed at but other organs as well. And, when Chinese medicines do not suit a person's constitution, they can have many different side effects.

PRESIDENT IKEDA: It seems that both types of medicines have their strong points. What's the best way to decide which kind of medicine to turn to?

KANAYA: Sudden or acute illnesses and infectious diseases respond best to Western medicine. On the other hand, when one does not really feel sick, but is still not in good condition, or when the cause of the illness cannot be identified, or in the case of some chronic disorder, Chinese medicine is often effective.

KODAMA: For example, anti-hypertensive drugs can effectively lower blood pressure. But when headaches, insomnia or numbness persist even after one's blood pressure drops, Chinese medicine can be very useful in relieving those symptoms.

PRESIDENT IKEDA: Does that mean we can use them together?

KATO: Yes, it does. In particular, those suffering from chronic illnesses and being treated with Western drugs can often use Chinese medicine to help eliminate any adverse side effects caused by those drugs, and also to improve their general physical condition so the dosage of Western drugs can be reduced.

KANAYA: It is important to remember, however, that a preparation of Chinese medicine needs to be specially tailored for the unique needs of each patient, so you should consult a specialist.

PRESIDENT IKEDA: There are many drugs, but all of them should only be used under the advice of a trusted specialist, who will be able to make the most effective use of them.

Earlier, I mentioned that Mr Toda had described the human body as one great pharmaceutical factory. The human body has a natural ability to heal itself. In Buddhism, this power is often described metaphorically as the function of Bodhisattva Medicine King (Jpn *Yakuo*). When we bring our lives in rhythm with the Mystic Law, the function of Bodhisattva Medicine King is strengthened and energised. And, when that happens, drugs no doubt work better, too.

KODAMA: I have seen many examples of that truth in other people and have experienced it in my own life as well.

PRESIDENT IKEDA: Next, let us discuss the proper methods of taking medicines.

They say that medicine is a two-edged sword. It can be beneficial or harmful, depending upon how it is used.

> The human body has a natural ability to heal itself. In Buddhism, this power is often described metaphorically as the function of Bodhisattva Medicine King (Jpn *Yakuo*). When we bring our lives in rhythm with the Mystic Law, the function of Bodhisattva Medicine King is trengthened and energised. And when that happens, drugs no doubt work better, too.

KANAYA: Yes. Side effects are a good example. Even drugs that are very effective can cause strong side effects in some patients.

PRESIDENT IKEDA: I guess it is a case of "One man's meat is another man's poison."

KODAMA: Yes. As far as the body is concerned, any drug is basically a foreign substance and, in that sense, slightly noxious. If the drug is not taken in the prescribed method or is taken in combination with some other substance that it should not be combined with, it can indeed become highly toxic to the body.

PRESIDENT IKEDA: I have heard that a number of poisonous substances are also approved for use in certain drugs.

KATO: Yes, an extremely small dosage of a poison is sometimes used as a medication for treating certain conditions. The dosage of the toxic substance has to be controlled with extreme care, because even the smallest overdose can prove fatal.

KODAMA: One good example is aconite, a substance derived from the monkshood plant. It has been used as a poison and also as a pain reliever since ancient times, and is still used in Chinese medicine.

Common Side Effects of Drugs

PRESIDENT IKEDA: What are some examples of the common side effects of drugs?

KODAMA: Stomach pains, constipation, diarrhoea, drowsiness and loss of concentration are common side effects of medication.

PRESIDENT IKEDA: Most doctors advise that pregnant women should avoid even cold medicines. Is that because of possible side effects?

KATO: Yes. Side effects are a concern. In addition, substances in the medication can also harm the foetus. Special care to avoid all drugs should be taken during the first trimester of pregnancy in particular.

KANAYA: Those who suffer from allergies or have liver or kidney problems are likely to be especially susceptible to side effects. Allergic reactions to drugs include rash, nausea and loss of appetite. In especially severe cases — though these are rare — the patient may lose consciousness.

PRESIDENT IKEDA: How can side effects be avoided?

KODAMA: First, let the doctor or pharmacist know if you are pregnant or suffer from allergies. After that, it is important to know about the medicine you will be taking, follow the directions concerning the dosage and other instructions, and always let them know what other medications you may be taking at the same time.

KATO: Yes, it is important to be informed about your medication. Unless you fully understand what it is and how it works, you may forget to take it or stop taking it, which could result in a serious worsening of your illness.

KANAYA: Whenever you receive a prescription, make certain to ask the doctor or pharmacist the name of the medicine, its effects, when it should be taken and what side effects you should be on the watch for and how you can prevent them.

PRESIDENT IKEDA: Drugs have such difficult names, don't they? Those long, scientific names somehow just make them sound so effective! But seriously, precisely because their names are not very revealing to the lay person, we must always be certain to receive a clear explanation of the drugs we take.

KANAYA: From next April [April 1997], a new pharmacy law will take effect in Japan. One of the provisions of the new law requires that pharmacists provide patients with the information they need to make proper use of the drugs they receive. I think that in some cases in the past, hospital pharmacies have been too busy to give patients clear and full explanations about the prescription drugs they dispense.

PRESIDENT IKEDA: The attitude with which pharmacists address patients is important, too. Some pharmacists, I have heard, are very bureaucratic or speak condescendingly to patients. When that happens, the explanation, no matter how thorough the content may be, isn't properly communicated to the patient. I hope all pharmacists will put themselves in the patient's shoes when they explain about prescription drugs, and do so in a courteous and considerate manner.

KODAMA: That is very true.

PRESIDENT IKEDA: Of course, patients must not simply be passive recipients of information, either. They need to make an active effort to protect their own health. As we said before, drugs can also be highly toxic. There is no need to become overly nervous, but if one has questions about taking a certain medication, one should voice them unhesitatingly and make sure one understands and is completely satisfied with the explanations before using that medication.

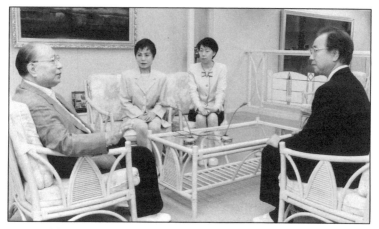

SGI President Ikeda (left), Soka Gakkai Doctors' Division Leader Dr Yoshio Kanaya (right) and pharmacists, Hitomi Kodama (2nd left) and Yuriko Kato (2nd right) . They discuss the state of Japanese medicines and drugs.

KATO: Yes, indeed. It is very important to communicate with your doctor and your pharmacist.

PRESIDENT IKEDA: Those who are in positions where they must advise or guide other people — not only in the fields of medicine and health services, but every field — have a duty to explain themselves fully, and people have the right to be fully convinced before following that advice or guidance. There has been all too little of this in Japanese culture to date, and I hope we will see a major change in this direction in the future.

And, this need for proper understanding and information is just as important when using over-the-counter remedies as well.

KATO: Yes. Again, the best thing to do is to ask the pharmacist for a full explanation of the particular medicine. In addition, read the usage directions and description of the medicine that comes with it fully and carefully. Many people just toss these directions away, but it is always a good idea to keep them as long as you have any of the medicine left.

PRESIDENT IKEDA: I think this is less true now, but in the past there were many very suspicious medicines peddled. There were also many unscrupulous, greedy doctors who earned large profits selling different kinds of quack medicines. In Japan, this practice has been referred to as 'ninefold medicine', meaning to profiteer on the sale of medicine by selling it many times what its original ingredients are actually worth. There is also an Edo-period (1600-1868) novel by an anonymous author, titled *Ninefold Medicine*, by the way.

KODAMA: What kind of novel?

PRESIDENT IKEDA: It tells the story of a very poor and conniving monk who was trying to come up with a scheme to make money. He recalled that once long ago when a fishbone had gotten stuck in his throat, he was able to dislodge it by taking a dose of flour mixed with red dirt. So, he struck upon the idea of making that 'medicine' and selling it as a cure for dislodging fishbones stuck in the throat. This 'wonder' remedy was a big hit; the monk soon gained fame as a 'doctor', and he made a great fortune.

KATO: Now, that is a good example of the old saying, "A priest always makes money on you, coming and going."

KANAYA: The fact that such a story was written during the Edo period shows that even then people thought of priests as venal and dishonest.

PRESIDENT IKEDA: Is there any 'ninefold medicine' still on sale today?

KANAYA: Not among official pharmaceuticals — nor, indeed, should there be!
Between ten and fifteen years are usually required to develop a new drug. Not only are new drugs tested rigorously for their effectiveness, safety and side effects, but strict quality-control measures are enforced after the drug is approved and manufactured. When we consider all the work that goes into producing safe, effective drugs, I think their prices are reasonable.

KODAMA: But I must say that among folk remedies and so-called health foods, there are many that are very expensive.

Follow Dosage Instructions Carefully

PRESIDENT IKEDA: As we have briefly touched on a little earlier, it is important when taking any medication to follow the dosage instructions, isn't it?

KANAYA: Yes. Depending upon the disease being treated, taking too much or forgetting a dose can be dangerous.

PRESIDENT IKEDA: Why are different drugs supposed to be taken at different times, most commonly before a meal, after a meal or between meals?

KATO: These times are indicated based on when ingesting the drug will be safest and most effective. For example, drugs that may upset the stomach are taken after a meal. Drugs that may have their effectiveness reduced or absorption impaired by stomach acids are usually taken before meals.

KANAYA: As a rule, 'after meals' means thirty minutes after eating and 'before meals' means thirty minutes before eating.

KODAMA: Drugs that help the stomach when it is empty or drugs that are particularly difficult for the system to absorb should be taken between meals.

PRESIDENT IKEDA: 'Between meals' means when the stomach is empty, then?

KODAMA: Yes. It is best to think of 'between meals' as about two hours after a meal.

PRESIDENT IKEDA: When taking a drug prescribed for 'after meals', is it absolutely necessary to eat a meal first?

KATO: You don't have to eat a lot, but to protect the stomach it is best to eat a little something — a cup of thick soup, a cookie or a cracker will do.

PRESIDENT IKEDA: Many people take their medicine with a cup of tea or a glass of juice.

KATO: Yes, but the safest method is to take a drug with a glass of lukewarm or cold water. The caffeine and tannin in coffee and tea can undermine the effect of many drugs.

KODAMA: And, juice and milk should both be avoided — especially when taking antibiotics. Milk reduces the effectiveness of antibiotics, and the acidity of orange juice and soft drinks may boost their effect.

PRESIDENT IKEDA: What effect does alcohol have on drugs?

KATO: When you are taking any medication, it is best to avoid the use of alcohol, which can strengthen or weaken the effect tremendously, depending upon the drug, and also cause adverse side effects.

KODAMA: Those taking drugs for diabetes and high blood pressure must be especially careful, because alcohol can cause sudden drops in blood-sugar level and blood pressure.

PRESIDENT IKEDA: What about the special needs of children and the elderly?

KANAYA: The dosages prescribed for over-the-counter drugs are often too strong for the elderly, who should get any drugs they may need from a clinic instead, if possible. If they do avail themselves of non-prescription remedies, however, it would probably be a good idea for them to start with a half-dosage. As far as children are concerned, the dosage directions on the package should be strictly followed, with the dosage kept within the recommended limit.

> The dosages prescribed for over-the-counter drugs are often too strong for the elderly, who should get any drugs they may need from a clinic instead, if possible.

PRESIDENT IKEDA: Where should medicines be stored?

KATO: The best place to store drugs is in a cool, dry place, away from direct sunlight.

KODAMA: The refrigerator is also a good place, except that children may mistake pills for candy and inadvertently eat them. To prevent this, you could perhaps put the medication in a special child-proof container.

KANAYA: When you have any drugs left over from a prescription after you stop taking it, do not keep them. Throw them away. Prescription drugs are for a specific person who has specific symptoms. If you have any left over, never give them to anyone else. When you no longer need the drug, throw any remainder away. And, of course, never accept medicine prescribed for anyone else, even if you seem to have the same symptoms.

KODAMA: Non-prescription drugs have a use-by date stamped on the package. Never use such drugs after that date, and if the drug is discoloured or shows any other change, throw it away even if it is still within the effective period.

PRESIDENT IKEDA: The advice to discard old prescriptions once one no longer needs them seems related to the principle that we should not become overly dependent on medication. A strong will to defeat one's sickness is also very important. On the other hand, it is a mistake to stop taking a prescription that you *do* need, isn't it?

KATO: It certainly is. It is dangerous to arbitrarily stop taking a prescription, to decrease the dosage, or to pick and choose from among your doctor's prescriptions. There are cases in which taking several varieties of drugs at once reduces side effects.

PRESIDENT IKEDA: The wrong combinations of drugs can also intensify side effects, can't they?

KODAMA: Yes. But most lay people do not know what drugs should not be taken together. So, I cannot stress enough how important it is when you need a prescription of medicine to let the doctor or pharmacist know about any other diseases or health problems you may have, and are currently being treated for and the medication you may be taking. The same holds true when buying over-the-counter remedies at the drugstore.

KATO: It is a good idea to jot down the names of the other medicines you are taking.

KANAYA: Especially for those with chronic illnesses, such as diabetes and high blood pressure, or for the elderly who have been on a drug regimen for a long time, I recommend keeping a 'medication notebook'.

PRESIDENT IKEDA: A medication notebook?

KODAMA: Yes. Any ordinary notebook will do. Just record the name of the drug, the name of the disease or condition, the date you received the drug, and the name of the hospital, clinic or pharmacy that dispensed it. You should also jot down a comment, particularly when a drug has caused a bad or allergic reaction. The record should include both prescription and non-prescription drugs.

PRESIDENT IKEDA: It is sort of a personal history of all the medication you have taken.

KANAYA: Yes, it is, and in fact, we call it a 'medication history'.

PRESIDENT IKEDA: In any case where you may be given medication of any kind, acquainting the doctor with detailed information on your medication status is very important, then.

KATO: Yes. For example, the fever-reducing drug you receive from an internist and the painkiller you receive from a dentist have the same effect, even though they may have different names. If you take both at the same time, you are taking double the dose you need.

PRESIDENT IKEDA: I also understand that while the same medicine might work for one person, it might not work for another, right?

KATO: This is most common with non-prescription drugs. A large person, for example, may not be affected by the standard dose. The severity of the person's symptoms and their general condition can also play a role in the drug's effectiveness.

KANAYA: There is also the so-called placebo effect to consider. A placebo is a dummy medicine. For example, if you give a patient a little bit of flour and tell him that it is a very effective drug, it may actually have a beneficial effect on him. This is the placebo effect.

KODAMA: On the other hand, if the patient does not understand the drug he is taking and feels anxious about its effects, he may claim that the symptoms persist even though, in fact, the drug is working.

PRESIDENT IKEDA: It is important to understand the drugs you are taking. Dr Norman Cousins (1912-1990), known as 'the conscience of America', was well known for his research on the placebo effect.
Soka Gakkai 2nd president Josei Toda, as I have mentioned before, used to say that the human body is a great pharmaceutical factory, and Dr Cousins

said that it is the best drugstore there is. Both were referring to the power of the body to heal itself.

Dr Cousins held that peace of mind, hope and the desire to live stimulates the body's recuperative powers to the greatest degree. They also increase the effectiveness of medicines. The word *placebo* derives, I believe, from the Latin word meaning 'to please'. In that sense, I think we can say that encouragement, which pleases and gladdens a sick person, is an all-purpose medicine.

Warm encouragement and support provide assurance and strength, hope and self-confidence. And, peace of mind and hope stimulate the patient's life force. Dr Cousins was emphatic on the point that the mind and body are one. He sought to demonstrate that truth scientifically. His belief is in accord with Buddhist teachings.

For example, though our body may be afflicted with a disease, if our mind is strong it can exert a positive influence on our physical condition. The strength and soundness of our attitude, of inner determination to be well, are very important. That is the secret to the lasting health of our life force.

No one can escape the sufferings of birth, old age, sickness and death. We all fall ill. We all have times when we are not up to top form. When one does become ill, the important thing is to bring forth strong prayer and wisdom aimed at overcoming that sickness. We should strengthen our life force through chanting dynamic, resonant *daimoku*, while actively availing ourselves of qualified medical expertise and sound treatment.

One should not fall into the trap of thinking that just by praying everything will be all right. The true power of prayer is only manifested to its fullest extent when it is accompanied by action. Buddhism is a teaching of reason.

Health is a daily effort, a combination of strong prayer and careful, practical action. I hope you will all live long, healthy lives. This is my keenest personal wish. Please live out your lives to the fullest. Doing so is a great challenge. Live long lives. No matter what happens, live vigorously right to the end, so that you can look back over your life and say, "What a wonderful life I had!" That is the true meaning of a healthy life.